Spelling 6

FOR YOUNG CATHOLICS

Written by
Seton Staff

SETON PRESS
Front Royal, VA

Executive Editor: Dr. Mary Kay Clark
Editors: Seton Staff

Seton Press
1350 Progress Drive
Front Royal, VA 22630

Phone: 540-636-9990
Fax: 540-636-1602

For more information, visit us on the Web at www.setonpress.com
Contact us by e-mail at info@setonpress.com

ISBN: 978-1-60704-009-5

Cover: *Teresa of Ávila*, Rubens

J.M.J.

Dedicated to the Sacred Heart of Jesus

Cathedral of Burgos

Barcelona, Spain

Spelling 6 for Young Catholics

Contents

NOTES for Parents and Teachers

Preface

Seton Home Study School is pleased to present *Spelling 6 for Young Catholics* in our series of spelling books. In light of the Vatican's directive for schools to incorporate the Faith throughout the curriculum, many of the stories and examples in this book include Catholic themes and culture. We hope that this presentation not only will facilitate learning correct spelling but also will supplement the awareness of Catholic history and culture as well as deepen the knowledge and practice of our Catholic Faith in daily life.

Pictures in This Book

In *Spelling 6*, we have attempted to provide knowledge of great Catholic architecture by showing churches and monasteries that are related to the saints discussed in the lessons. Historically, the great art academies have taught that there are four fundamental forms of art: painting, sculpture, architecture, and engraving. Most of Seton Home Study School's books contain great paintings that illustrate the stories in these books. However, in addition to the great oil paintings and sculptures that Catholic artists have created, there is also an abundance of magnificent Catholic architecture. This architecture is seen most notably in churches and monasteries around the world.

In some cases, the churches shown in this book are the churches where saints attended Mass. In other cases, they are churches named after a particular saint, as in the case of the Blessed Mother or Saint Michael. Still other churches contain relics, usually the tombs of the saints. We hope that as you read about these holy men and women, the pictures of the churches will bring you closer to them.

Introduction

Spelling 6 for Young Catholics utilizes the phonics system of learning to spell. Phonics is a method of teaching reading and spelling based on sounds. Phonics focuses on the study of the sounds of speech. Listening and hearing sounds is key in this endeavor. We refer to this ability as the auditory skill, that is, one based on hearing and differentiating sounds in words.

The *Spelling for Young Catholics* series uses the phonics method and is intended to provide a solid foundation for correct spelling usage. Through the lessons in this book, your student will learn to spell multi-syllable words containing regular and irregular spelling patterns. Encourage your student to build upon this foundation of spelling rules and word patterns. A comprehensive summary of spelling rules is provided in the back of this book. Encourage your student to review these rules regularly.

It is helpful to remember that good spelling has little to do with being "smart," but rather is a skill that almost everyone can master. Remind your student that incorrect spelling results in clear ideas becoming unclear, causing readers to believe that a writer is either incompetent or does not have the ability or concern to pay attention to details. Most employers will discard any job application that contains spelling errors. If someone at the Kennedy Space Center in Cape Canaveral, Florida, wrote that the **p** rings, rather than **o** rings, in the space shuttle were iced, the safety engineer would be fired immediately. The spell checker on a computer cannot detect the difference between "**p** rings" and "**o** rings."

Most students at this age are moving onto the computer in doing their schoolwork, but we encourage you to not allow them to use the spell checker, especially since it does not always recognize incorrect spelling. Teach your student the importance of mastering correct spelling, so that general communication problems in reading and writing do not occur. Anyone who must struggle to read something because of incorrect spelling will soon give up trying to read it.

Learning to spell frequently used words will enable your student to spell other words correctly. As your student becomes aware of spelling rules and correct spelling patterns, keep a dictionary within easy reach. Encourage your student to look up words in the dictionary to verify the spelling or meaning.

Spelling, Phonics, and Vocabulary

When explaining the difference between spelling and phonics, point out the following. ***Spelling*** emphasizes the *different spellings of the same sounds*, such as the sound /**uu**/ in the words b**oo**k and b**u**sh. ***Phonics*** distinguishes between *different sounds in words that are similarly spelled*. A phonics lesson would take words like b**oo**k /**uu**/ and b**oo**t /**oo**/ with the same spelling of the letters **oo**, and then would sort them by the phonetic sounds in these words, that is, /**uu**/ and /**oo**/ in this case. The letters **oo** are the same in each spelling word but are pronounced differently.

Parents are sometimes inclined to use the vocabulary words rather than the spelling words for the weekly spelling tests. The difference between teaching spelling lessons using spelling words and teaching spelling using vocabulary words is in the grouping of words. For example, the word c**a**t may be included in a spelling lesson on spelling the /**aa**/ sound, as well as a vocabulary lesson on animals. In the spelling lesson, the word c**a**t is compared with words such as d**a**d and c**a**b. This comparison of spelling words helps the student learn the spelling rule for a number of similar words. Spelling a mixture of words in a vocabulary list does not reinforce any spelling rules.

Pronunciation

In this spelling book, letter combinations are used as pronunciation symbols. Pronunciation symbols for vowel and consonant sounds vary somewhat among different dictionaries. You may refer your student to the pronunciation symbols used in your dictionary at home and or school.

For the purpose of spelling lessons, it is beneficial to teach your student to exaggerate the pronunciation of the unstressed vowels while looking at and reading the word. In doing so, your student will likely associate the pronunciation with the correct spelling of the vowel. The word *Catholic*, for example, technically has three spelling syllables. When pronouncing for correct spelling, your student can use the exaggerated three-syllable pronunciation (*Cath-o-lic*) as an auditory device as well as a visual memory device as he or she looks at the written word and pronounces it. In daily language, of course, your student should pronounce these words correctly. Only when pronouncing for a spelling memory device should your student pronounce the words with an exaggerated pronunciation.

Pronunciation Symbols

Note the following pronunciation symbols or combinations of letters within a pair of slashes for the vowel sounds. It is not necessary for your student to memorize a specific set of pronunciation symbols. It is important that your student be able to identify the sounds and memorize the spellings that represent each sound.

Short Vowel Sounds

the /**aa**/ sound in at
the /**eh**/ sound in egg
the /**ih**/ sound in it
the /**ah**/ sound in ox
the /**uh**/ sound in us

Long Vowel Sounds

the /**ay**/ sound in ate
the /**ee**/ sound in eve
the /**iy**/ sound in ice
the /**oh**/ sound in oak
the /**yoo**/ sound in use

Other Vowel Sounds

the /**aw**/ sound in awe
the /**oo**/ sound in ooze
the /**uu**/ sound in book
the /**ou**/ sound in out
the /**oi**/ sound in oil

Some dictionaries use different pronunciation symbols for vowels followed by the consonant **r** because the pronunciation of some **r**-controlled words varies among different dialects. In this book, the pronunciation symbol for the vowel sound is combined with the symbol for the sound of **r**. Note this combination in the following symbols for **r**-controlled sounds:

the /**ahr**/ sound in ark
the /**uhr**/ sound in urn
the /**ehr**/ sound in air
the /**eer**/ sound in ear
the /**ohr**/ sound in oar

The *Spelling* 6 Book

The *Spelling 6* book contains thirty-six lessons. In each quarter, there are eight lessons of new words and one lesson of review. Each weekly lesson consists of exercises, one for each of the first four days of the week. The fifth day of each week is a quiz day. Please administer a spelling quiz on that day.

The last lesson of each quarter is a quarterly review in preparation for the quarterly test, which should be administered four times a year. An audio dictation of test words is available online on the Seton website for enrolled students.

In the back of this book is a summary of the spelling rules to be learned. Your student should refer to this comprehensive summary of rules often. Also, notice the Answer Key for the exercises.

The Daily Exercises

Each weekly lesson is divided into four days, each day containing an exercise. The fifth day of the week is reserved for a spelling quiz. Give your student the following directions.

Day One. Exercise A: Sort by Syllable, Sort by Spelling, or Sort by Sound

Exercise A presents a list of 21 words, and sometimes a spelling rule that pertains to each of the words being presented. Read and think about the rule provided at the top of the page and how it applies to each word in the list. Then follow the instructions for the exercise. As you pronounce each word, pay attention to the sound you hear yourself making. Look at the word, pronounce it, and spell it out loud. Repeat the process while looking at the word. Next, in the blanks provided, sort each word from the word list, following the specific instructions given for that exercise. Check the spelling of each word.

Day Two. Exercise B: Definitions

The exercise for Day Two shows a list of definitions. Select the word from the list of words provided for the week that matches the definition provided. You are encouraged to use your dictionary to help you understand the correct meaning of the word. This is an important exercise for writing the spelling words correctly and for understanding the meaning of the words at the same time.

Day Three. Exercise C: Missing Words

The exercise for Day Three asks you to write the missing word in each sentence. Read each sentence carefully. Check the list of words and decide which one is the correct word to give the proper meaning to the sentence. A list word is to be used only once in the exercise. Not all list words will be used. Write the word in the column next to each sentence. As you write it, say the word. Now read the complete sentence, look at the word, and repeat it. Spell each word out loud without looking at the word list. Check the spelling. If you misspelled a word, erase it and write it correctly. Continue this exercise with each additional sentence.

Day Four. Exercise D: Story Time

Exercise D consists of stories containing words that demonstrate the spelling rule or examples pertaining to the lesson. The words demonstrating the spelling are underlined in the body of the story. Pay attention to the spelling rule or pattern and notice how it applies to each underlined word. For additional optional practice, on a separate sheet of paper, write the words from the spelling list.

Day Five: Spelling Quiz

On Day Five of each weekly lesson, parents or teachers should administer a spelling quiz by dictating to the student each word from the list of spelling words. Each word should be pronounced by itself, pronounced in the context of a sentence, and then pronounced by itself again. The student should listen to each word as it is dictated and write it on a separate sheet of paper. The parent or teacher may average the quiz grades for the quarter. After the spelling quiz is corrected, any misspelled words should be correctly rewritten five times each. Enrolled students are provided quarterly tests with their lesson plans. Orally dictated words, as well as crossword puzzles for the spelling words, are provided online.

Memorizing Spelling Words

Experts tell us that in order to learn to spell most effectively, it is best to combine the use of three of our senses. We use our auditory sense (hearing) when we pronounce the word or hear it pronounced; we use the visual sense (seeing) when we look at the word and make a mental image of it (memory); and we use the kinesthetic sense (touch) when we physically write the word. Since identifying the sounds in words phonetically is an auditory (hearing) exercise, whereas memorizing the spelling of words is a visual (seeing) exercise, we can use visual aids, such as flash cards, in learning how to spell. Here are the recommended steps to follow:

1. Write spelling words on flash cards and then place them on a wall or poster board in front of you so that you will use your eyes to move from right to left.
2. Look at the word closely. Break the word up into syllables and notice any smaller words within the word.
3. Take a mental snapshot of the word. Blink your eyes like the shutter of a camera and hold your eyes closed for a few seconds. Then say the word out loud.
4. When you are ready, cover the word on the wall and look at the same space. Read the word out loud phonetically as you see it on your visual memory screen. As you pronounce it, how does it look? Repeat the process, if necessary.
5. Test yourself by writing the word out on paper. Now take off the cover and check it. If you made a mistake repeat the process.
6. To implant the spelling in your phonetic-auditory memory, say the word out loud, or sing to a favorite tune. Spell the letters of the word out loud as you commit it to memory.

The word should now be solidly in place in your visual, kinesthetic and auditory memory.

CATHEDRAL OF BARCELONA

SPAIN

NAME

LESSON 1

/oo/ as in noon

- bloom ✓
- droop ✓
- fireproof ✓
- gloom ✓
- groove ✓
- homeschool ✓
- ooze ✓
- proof ✓
- roof ✓
- roost ✓
- scoop ✓
- shoot ✓
- smooth ✓
- stool ✓
- toothbrush ✓
- zookeeper ✓
- whom ✓
- youth ✓
- youthful ✓
- jewelry ✓

BONUS

- newscast ✓

The sound of /**oo**/ may be spelled **oo**, **o**, **ou**, or **ew**, as in n**oo**n, wh**o**m, y**ou**th, and j**ew**el.

A SORT BY SPELLING

Each syllable has its own sound/spelling. Identify the syllables in each word. Sort the words by the spelling of the /**oo**/ sound.

oo	bloom
	droop
	fireproof
	gloom
	groove
	homeschool
	ooze
	proof
	roof
	roost
	scoop
	shoot
	stool
	toothbrush
	zookeeper
	smooth
o	whom
ou	youth
	youthful
ew	jewelry
	newscast

21/21

B DEFINITIONS

Given below are definitions to the words found in the word list. Write the appropriate word in the space provided next to the definition.

to dig or scrape out	1. scoop
to forcefully throw a projectile with a weapon	2. shoot
without bump or roughness; even	3. smooth
a three-legged seat without a back	4. stool
unable to be burned	5. fireproof
to produce flowers; blossom	6. bloom
to conduct one's education at home	7. homeschool
to seep slowly out, as said of a liquid	8. ooze
evidence that something is true	9. proof
darkness; sad mood	10. gloom
the state of being young; people who are young	11. youth
filled with youth; young	12. youthful
ornaments for the body	13. jewelry
a narrow channel in a surface; rut	14. groove
the top cover of a building	15. roof
to settle down to rest or sleep (usually refers to birds)	16. roost
a brush used to clean the teeth	17. toothbrush
a person who cares for animals in a zoo	18. zookeeper
the objective case of *who*	19. whom
to sag or hang down	20. droop
a televised news message	21. newscast

NAME Isabella

C SENTENCES

In each sentence below, there is a blank corresponding to one of the words found in the word list. Write the missing word in the space next to the sentence.

Good Friday brought ___ upon the earth as Jesus died on the Cross.	1. gloom
The roses will ___ beside the statue of Our Lady.	2. bloom
Mrs. Hunter decided to ___ her eight children.	3. homeschool
David picked up three ___ stones from the creek to use in his slingshot.	4. smooth
The mud began to ___ between Tommy's toes as he walked barefoot in the rain.	5. ooze
St. Thomas wanted ___ that Jesus appeared to the other Apostles in the Upper Room.	6. proof
The friends of the paralyzed man lowered him through the ___ to see Jesus.	7. roof
Jesus said, "The kingdom of heaven is like a tree, in which all the birds of the air come to ___."	8. roost
Johnny tried to ___ out the last of the ice cream from the container.	9. scoop
The baby's eyelids began to ___ as he lay in the arms of his mother.	10. droop
St. Joseph showed the boy Jesus how to make a ___ and a table.	11. stool
The ___ safe will keep our precious photos protected.	12. fireproof
St. John Bosco loved working with the ___ and teaching them about Jesus.	13. youthful
The young Indian used his bow and arrow to ___ the deer.	14. shoot
Queen Esther wore beautiful ___ when she went to meet her king.	15. jewelery

D STORY TIME

Read the following story, paying attention to the underlined words. Notice how they use the spelling rule to the right.

/oo/ as in n**oo**n, wh**o**m, y**ou**th, j**ew**el

The Crusades

The Crusades were military expeditions of Christian armies <u>whose</u> ambition was to rescue the Holy Land from the Turks. These holy wars extended <u>through</u> the eleventh, twelfth, and thirteenth centuries.

Many of the nobility wholeheartedly enrolled as Crusaders. Their shields were marked with the sign of the Cross. In their eagerness, many people made the journey without proper provisions. Some starved on the way, and others had <u>to</u> return home.

The Crusades were successful in that many people earned graces. They were not successful in permanently returning the Holy Land <u>to</u> the Christians. They did, however, bring about many changes in Europe. A <u>new</u> <u>route</u> to the East was discovered. The absence of the nobility during the Crusades also resulted in a change in the feudal system of government in Europe. Thus the Crusades encouraged the great ages of exploration and discovery which followed.

Monastery of Vezelay, France

St. Bernard of Clairvaux preached the Second Crusade here on Palm Sunday, 1146.

VEZELAY INTERIOR

VEZELAY, FRANCE

LESSON

2

/uu/ in book, /oo/ in tune

barefoot
bullet
bulletin
bullion
cushion
driftwood
fulfill
good-by
good-bye
livelihood
lunar
movable
pursue
pursuing
route
routine
salute
truly
tulip
tuna

BONUS

dilute

NAME

The sound /**uu**/ may be spelled **oo**, or **u** as in b**oo**k and b**u**llet.
The sound /**oo**/ may be spelled **u**, **ou**, or **o**, as in t**u**ne r**ou**te, and m**o**vable.

A SORT BY SPELLING / VOWEL SOUND

Each syllable has its own sound/spelling. Sort the words by the letters **oo**, **u**, **ou**, or **o**.

oo	
u	
ou	
o	

B DEFINITIONS

Given below are definitions to the words found in the word list. Write the appropriate word in the space provided next to the definition.

a public notice from an official source	1.
an often repeated way of doing things	2.
gold or silver, usually in bars	3.
a soft pillow or stuffed pad	4.
wood found floating in a body of water	5.
to do something as a duty or promise or command	6.
an expression spoken when people leave each other	7.
a means of support to live	8.
to chase after or follow	9.
without shoes	10.
able to be moved	11.
to make thinner by adding liquid	12.
chasing after or following	13.
relating to the moon	14.
a road or way	15.
a projectile launched from a firearm	16.
a type of flower of various colors	17.
a respectful greeting, often a bow or gesture	18.
an accepted form of the usual spelling of "good-bye"	19.
really, actually	20.
a kind of food from a large ocean-dwelling fish	21.

NAME ______________________________

C SENTENCES

In each sentence below, there is a blank corresponding to one of the words found in the word list. Write the missing word in the space next to the sentence.

All Catholics must ___ the requirement of fasting before Communion.	1.
Jason found ___ cast ashore on the beach, along with shells and starfish.	2.
The army private will ___ the general as a sign of respect.	3.
It was clear to all that St. Margaret Mary ___ loved the Sacred Heart of Jesus.	4.
Mrs. O'Reilly made a soft ___ for her couch.	5.
Jacinta and Francisco often would run ___ in the fields with the sheep.	6.
The ___ is a very popular flower during Eastertime.	7.
After staying at Corinth, St. Paul said ___ and sailed to Syria.	8.
Mother would fix ___ sandwiches for us to eat on Fridays during Lent.	9.
The grand piano was not ___, and had to be left in the old church.	10.
We saw the ___ eclipse.	11.
To get to the grotto of Our Lady, you must take the ___ on the left.	12.
The Egyptian king commanded his men to ___ the Israelites into the desert.	13.
It is the ___ for our family to say the Rosary every night.	14.
The policeman wore his ___-proof vest while he was on duty.	15.

D STORY TIME

Read the following story, paying attention to the underlined words. Notice how they use the spelling rule to the right.

/**uu**/ in b**oo**k, b**u**llet
/**oo**/ in t**u**ne, r**ou**te, m**o**vable

Prayer

We should always pray. Every action we perform and every word our tongues utter should be offered to God. We should begin and end every day with prayer.

Not only does God wish us to pray, but He also has given us a command to pray. We can gain plenary and partial indulgences when we say certain prayers. These prayers are the Our Father, Hail Mary, the Apostles' Creed, the Confiteor, the Acts of Faith, Hope, Charity, and Contrition, and the Angelus. The greatest prayer of all is the Holy Sacrifice of the Mass.

Songs and hymns can be prayers, too. If we <u>look</u> in a <u>hymnbook</u> or a Catholic <u>songbook</u>, we might find some prayerful songs which we can sing easily.

Prayers do not need to be long. A favorite short Mass prayer is "Lamb of God." Our growth as Christians depends on our faithfulness in prayer. If we pray with attention and confidence, God will accept our offering and grant us grace according to our needs.

LESSON

3

/**oh**/ as in home

approach
cello
chose
envelope
foe
goes
homely
homemade
homogenize
loaf
loaves
mediocre
motion
noticeable
nowhere
obedience
old-fashioned
omitted
oversee
prose

BONUS

omission

NAME ____________________

The long vowel sound /**oh**/ may be spelled **o**, **oa**, or **oe**, as in h**o**me, l**oa**f, and g**oe**s.

A SORT BY SPELLING

Each syllable has its own sound/spelling. Sort the words by the letters for the sound of /**oh**/.

o	
oa	
oe	

B DEFINITIONS

Given below are definitions to the words found in the word list. Write the appropriate word in the space provided next to the definition.

to come closer to	1.
made at home; not store-bought	2.
an act of obeying	3.
a flat paper container for papers or letters	4.
to look down upon, survey	5.
selected, picked	6.
leaves, departs	7.
not very attractive, plain	8.
left out; deleted	9.
a large stringed instrument related to the violin	10.
something left out	11.
to make even or the same	12.
a quantity of bread, usually in a rectangular or oblong shape	13.
not outstanding; second-rate	14.
enemy	15.
able to be observed	16.
movement or activity	17.
not anywhere	18.
more than one mass of bread; plural of "loaf"	19.
ordinary spoken or written language	20.
not modern; out-of-date; pertaining to former times	21.

NAME ______

C SENTENCES

In each sentence below, there is a blank corresponding to one of the words found in the word list. Write the missing word in the space next to the sentence.

The Fourth Commandment is about ___.	1.
The cellist placed his ___ on the floor between his knees.	2.
Jesus said to the apostles, "You did not choose Me; I ___ you."	3.
Mr. Clark ___ the last question from the exam, which relieved the students.	4.
The priest ___ to say Mass once a week for the missionary church in the mountains.	5.
The local grocery store bought the ___ jam from the farmer's wife.	6.
Their ___ invaded the country from the north.	7.
The story is an example of well-written ___.	8.
St. John was the first to ___ the empty tomb of Jesus.	9.
Jesus blessed the five barley ___ and two fish, and gave them to the people.	10.
The constant bumpy ___ of the old farm wagon made the children sick.	11.
When we ___ milk, the fat is evenly spread out.	12.
A sin of ___ is not doing something we know we should have done.	13.
The holiness of Mother Teresa of Calcutta was certainly ___ to all who knew her.	14.
The wedding ring, which slipped off the bride's finger, was ___ to be found.	15.

D STORY TIME

Read the following story, paying attention to the underlined words. Notice how they use the spelling rule to the right.

/oh/ in h**o**me, l**oa**f, g**oe**s

The Council of Clermont

At the Council of Clermont, Pope Urban gave instructions to those who would go on the Crusades. The clergy were to participate in the Crusades only with their bishop's consent. Lay people were directed to obtain the blessing of a priest before their departure. The participants were to wear a cross of cloth upon their outer dress. For this reason, they were called Crusaders, from the Latin word *crux* meaning cross.

Popular preachers immediately spread the appeal of Pope Urban II. Men like Peter the Hermit toured Europe announcing the Crusade. Indulgences and Church protection of property were promised to those who undertook the journey.

Clermont Cathedral

Clermont, France

Cathedral of Santiago de Compostela

Galicia, Spain

LESSON

4

/ou/ as in out

allowance
arouse
bough
bounce
council
counsel
crouch
doubt
drown
foul
how's
mound
nowadays
ounce
pound
prowl
scout
scowl
shout
shower

BONUS

sprout

NAME ______________________________

The sound of /**ou**/ may be spelled **ou** or **ow**, as in **ou**t and h**ow**.

A SORT BY SPELLING

Each syllable has its own sound/spelling. Sort the words by the spelling of the /**ou**/ sound.

ou	
ow	

B DEFINITIONS

Given below are definitions to the words found in the word list. Write the appropriate word in the space provided next to the definition.

to call out loudly	1.
a committee or official group of people	2.
to squat down	3.
money given at regular intervals	4.
to grow or spring up	5.
to move about in a secretive manner	6.
to die by being submersed in a liquid	7.
to make a dark look or frown	8.
to spring back, such as a ball	9.
disgusting or unclean	10.
advice or guidance	11.
a contraction for "how is"	12.
a large tree branch	13.
the standard English unit of weight	14.
a pile or large lump	15.
in modern times; not in the past	16.
a small fluid measurement	17.
to disbelieve; to be uncertain	18.
to awaken	19.
bathing oneself by means of water spraying from a spout	20.
someone who goes ahead to check out an area	21.

NAME

C SENTENCES

In each sentence below, there is a blank corresponding to one of the words found in the word list. Write the missing word in the space next to the sentence.

To surprise the enemy, Gideon urged his soldiers to ___ down and hide.	1.
Bob left the garbage in the garage and now it has a ___ smell.	2.
The robin built her nest in the old oak tree on a very thin ___.	3.
Julius Caesar would often ___ at the Senators whenever they talked about the Roman Republic.	4.
The basketball player continued to ___ the ball down the court!	5.
My brother used his ___ to buy a new skateboard.	6.
The pitcher is set to throw from the ___.	7.
The St. James Church ___ decided to buy new vestments for the priests.	8.
An ___ of milk was placed in a bottle to nurse the newborn calf back to health.	9.
The ___ reported to General Lee that Grant's army was hiding in the woods.	10.
Since Jimmy thought about becoming a priest, he sought the ___ of his spiritual director.	11.
Every morning, Mother must ___ the boys from their sleep.	12.
My brother Jeff takes a ___ in the morning before leaving for work.	13.
St. Joan of Arc did not ___ that the voices which spoke to her were from Heaven.	14.
With the present heat wave ___, one cannot be too careful to avoid the sun.	15.

D STORY TIME

Read the following story, paying attention to the underlined words. Notice how they use the spelling rule to the right.

/ou/ in **ou**t, h**ow**

The Pilgrimage

Making a pilgrimage was a very common devotion and personal sacrifice during the Middle Ages. It was a long journey, usually made on foot or on horseback, to some Catholic shrine. The favorite pilgrimage was the one to the Holy Land. The pilgrims loved this hallowed land where <u>Our</u> Lord spent His life. They visited each shrine that was erected to commemorate a particular event of <u>Our</u> Lord's life.

The Church gave special blessings or indulgences for pilgrims, <u>out</u> of the Treasury of the Church. The temporal punishment which was due for sin was forgiven through these special indulgences. Today, we can still satisfy for some punishment due for sin by making special pilgrimages to Catholic shrines and holy places.

In the eleventh century, the Turks captured Jerusalem. When these unbelievers took control of the city, they refused to give Christians the freedom they formerly had enjoyed. They robbed, killed or placed in bondage those who tried to visit the shrines. They even desecrated the sacred relics in the holy places. At last, the armies of Christendom marched on the Turks in an attempt to rescue the Holy Land. The Christian people were <u>aroused</u> to act, and they never <u>doubted</u> that God would bless their efforts.

LESSON

5

/oi/ as in oil
/ou/ as in out

appointment
account
android
boycott
boysenberry
compound
decoy
denounce
employ
enjoyable
foyer
hoist
household
renown
touchdown
tower
turquoise
undoubtedly
warehouse
whereabouts

BONUS

discount

NAME

The sound **/oi/** may be spelled **oi** or **oy**, as in **oi**l and b**oy**.
The sound **/ou/** may be spelled **ou** or **ow**, as in **ou**t and h**ow**.

A SORT BY SPELLING

Each syllable has its own sound/spelling. Sort the words by the spelling of the sounds.

oi	
oy	
ou	
ow	

B DEFINITIONS

Given below are definitions to the words found in the word list. Write the appropriate word in the space provided next to the definition.

a record of a person's money kept by a bank; a statement listing purchases	1.
to pay someone in return for services; to provide with a paying job	2.
a substance made up of two or more elements	3.
the location of something or someone	4.
pleasant, satisfying	5.
a predetermined date to meet someone	6.
to lift or raise up	7.
an object designed to distract or lure into a trap	8.
fame or glory	9.
a score achieved in football	10.
a tall building	11.
a robot designed to look human	12.
to condemn or criticize	13.
a lobby or entrance hall	14.
those in a family who live in one house	15.
a blue-green color; a gem of a blue-green color	16.
a type of dark-colored berry	17.
certainly, unquestionably	18.
a large building where goods are stored	19.
to join with others in refusing to support a group or a country	20.
an amount taken off a regular price	21.

NAME ____________________

C SENTENCES

In each sentence below, there is a blank corresponding to one of the words found in the word list. Write the missing word in the space next to the sentence.

The parish decided to ____ the bookstore because it sells anti-Catholic books.	1.
The chemistry teacher showed us how a ____ can be broken down into its elements.	2.
The Roman soldier at the foot of the Cross declared that Jesus was ____ the Son of God.	3.
Ann placed her allowance into her bank savings ____.	4.
My mother placed a small home altar in the ____, just in front of the winding stairs.	5.
It was easier to ____ the large bed up the stairs with the help of four strong men.	6.
St. Therese, the Little Flower, came from a very prayerful and happy ____.	7.
The home team scored a ____ in the last seconds to win the football game.	8.
The ____ was first developed by a man named Rudolf Boysen, and grown in California.	9.
The people built the ____ of Babel in order to reach the heavens.	10.
The family vacation to Arizona was a very ____ one, though it was very hot.	11.
The region once known as Persia remains the best place to mine the gem, ____.	12.
The stained glass windows were kept in a ____ while the new church was being built.	13.
The factory will ____ several hundred people who live in the town.	14.
The shrine gift shop gave us a ____ on all the saint books we purchased.	15.

D STORY TIME

Read the following story, paying attention to the underlined words. Notice how they use the spelling rule to the right.

/oi/ in oil, boy
/ou/ in out, how

Popes and Emperors

Two great powers had arisen in Western Christendom, the Papacy and the Empire. Undoubtedly, the Church had attained tremendous influence, which was enhanced by the Crusades. From the time of Charlemagne and Otto I, the Empire had also accumulated power and prestige. A struggle for supremacy was inevitable, even after the victory of the popes against lay control. The new conflict raged for about one hundred years.

The struggle was not a religious war. The opponents of the pope acknowledged the spiritual superiority of the Church. However, in their attempts to control Italy, the emperors tried to undermine the temporal authority of the popes, compounding the problem for the people. In following these tactics, the emperors proceeded to "depose" popes and to appoint anti-popes. The papacy, therefore, insisted on its right to denounce and depose rulers who violated the freedom of the Church and disrupted Christian unity.

LESSON

6

/ay/ as in behave
/aa/ as in apt

acquaintance
acquainted
remainder
ancient
anyway
associate
behave
behavior
annual
answered
antarctic
apparatus
apt
asterisk
athletics
avenue
bachelor
bankruptcy
banquet
beatitude

BONUS

beatify

NAME

The long vowel sound **/ay/** may be spelled **a** + consonant + silent **e**, **ai**, or **ay**, as in beh**a**ve, rem**ai**n, and w**ay**. The short vowel sound **/aa/** may be spelled **a**, as in **a**pt..

A SORT BY VOWEL SOUND

Each syllable has its own sound/spelling. Sort the words by the long sound **/ay/** and the short sound **/aa/**.

/ay/	

/aa/	

B DEFINITIONS

Given below are definitions to the words found in the word list. Write the appropriate word in the space provided next to the definition.

a person one knows slightly	1.
to conduct oneself properly	2.
to declare a person has attained the blessedness of Heaven	3.
a remaining group or part	4.
the state of being without money and unable to pay debts	5.
very old	6.
the way someone or something acts	7.
having to do with the Earth's South Pole	8.
replied, responded	9.
at any rate, nevertheless	10.
equipment	11.
competent and clever	12.
a partner	13.
a symbol, resembling a star, used to refer to a note	14.
physical exercise, sports	15.
statement made by Jesus about blessings and rewards	16.
a wide street	17.
happening every year	18.
to be familiar with	19.
an unmarried man	20.
a formal dinner for a special occasion	21.

NAME

C SENTENCES

In each sentence below, there is a blank corresponding to one of the words found in the word list. Write the missing word in the space next to the sentence.

St. Elizabeth of Hungary learned at a very young age how to ___ in the court of the king.	1.
The ___ of the pie was eaten by Dad when he came home from work.	2.
St. Monica prayed for many years that the pagan ___ of her son, Augustine, would change.	3.
Peter ___ Jesus, "You know everything, Lord. You know that I love you."	4.
The ___ Circle, very close to the South Pole, is considered the coldest place on earth.	5.
The diver's breathing ___ was tested and checked very carefully before the dive.	6.
The ___ student was very clever in his answer to the test question.	7.
As a young man, Pope John Paul II was very involved in ___; he liked to ski and play soccer.	8.
The ___ Festival of Our Lady of Guadalupe was held in the church hall.	9.
After being a ___ for most of his life, my uncle finally decided to marry.	10.
The small parish was saved from ___ after a very large and generous donation.	11.
Zacheus, the tax collector, invited Jesus to a ___ at his house.	12.
The ___ pyramids built by the Egyptians are a great sign of man's skill and intelligence.	13.
Christopher Columbus was ___ with Queen Isabella of Spain, who helped finance his first voyage.	14.
One ___ that Jesus gave us is, "Blessed are the merciful, for they shall obtain mercy."	15.

D STORY TIME

Read the following story, paying attention to the underlined words. Notice how they use the spelling rule to the right.

/ay/ in beh**a**ve, rem**ai**n, w**ay**
/aa/ in **a**pt

Cathedrals

Cathedrals are large, ornate churches built to express man's faith and our devotion to saints and martyrs. Because our faith in God is such a beautiful thing, Catholics want to make their churches as beautiful as possible. That is why long ago Catholics started building cathedrals.

These cathedrals are built all over Europe. Among these buildings, there is the widest possible variation in structure, ornamentation, height, vaulting, spire, and sculpture. Yet they are all beautiful. They were built in many different styles, the most famous being the Gothic style, such as the one at Chartres.

This most beautiful style of architecture, with its pointed arches, gives grace and beauty to the church. Heavy columns were replaced by graceful pillars. The wall space is filled with jewel-like windows, and its stone ceiling is supported from the outside by flying buttresses.

We can be proud of Catholics' wonderful achievements.

LESSON

7

/ah/ as in ox

bothered
approximate
blossom
chopped
conference
content
contest
cooperate
cooperation
dropped
fossil
holiday
optimism
otter
patriotic
policy
prompt
shock
solid
sovereign

BONUS

volume

NAME ______________________

The short vowel sound **/ah/** may be spelled by **o**, as in **ox**.

A SORT BY SYLLABLE

Each syllable has its own sound/spelling. Identify the syllables in each word. Sort the words by the number of syllables.

1	
2	
3	
4	
5	

B DEFINITIONS

Given below are definitions to the words found in the word list. Write the appropriate word in the space provided next to the definition.

the loudness of something	1.
nearly correct; not quite exact	2.
to work along with someone else	3.
the act of working along with someone else	4.
firm and unyielding	5.
to let an object fall from one's hands	6.
happy and satisfied	7.
to bloom; the flower on a plant	8.
the highest or supreme ruler	9.
small furry animal that likes the water	10.
a festival or feast day	11.
a habit of expecting things to turn out well	12.
full of reverence and fervor for one's country	13.
a plan or way of doing something	14.
a large meeting of people with similar interests	15.
annoyed or troubled by something	16.
remains of a plant or animal preserved in rock	17.
timely; without delay	18.
a sudden strong surprise; jolt	19.
a competition or challenge	20.
cut by being struck quickly again and again, as with a knife or ax	21.

NAME ______________________

C SENTENCES

In each sentence below, there is a blank corresponding to one of the words found in the word list. Write the missing word in the space next to the sentence.

The homeschooling ___ was held in San Antonio where mothers gave tips about educating their children.	1.
It was the ___ of the company that all men wear a suit and tie to work.	2.
The carpenter said he will ___ with the contractor to remodel the kitchen in one month.	3.
The increasing ___ of the band music caused the neighbors to complain.	4.
The wood was ___ into logs and stacked very carefully for winter.	5.
The ___ between the Dominicans and the Franciscans helped to reform the monasteries during the 1200's.	6.
The ___ on the rose bush bloomed just before the winter snows came.	7.
She was ___ for her job interview, so that no one had to wait.	8.
John Philip Sousa wrote ___ songs, including the military march, "Stars and Stripes Forever."	9.
Knights of the Middle Ages would often have a ___ to entertain with their fencing skills.	10.
The young boy ___ the statue of St. Joseph on the floor, but it did not break.	11.
The raising of Lazarus from the dead was a ___ to the high priests of the temple.	12.
The kitten appeared ___ while sleeping on grandma's lap.	13.
St. Francis Xavier was known for his incredible ___ as he tried to convert the heathens.	14.
God is King and ___ over the entire universe.	15.

D **STORY TIME**

Read the following story, paying attention to the underlined words. Notice how they use the spelling rule to the right.

/ah/ in **o**x

St. Thomas Aquinas

St. Thomas was a Dominican who was very scholarly and a great educator. His many splendid books are read by more scholars today than in his own lifetime.

However, he was not always regarded as such. After St. Thomas entered the Dominican order against the will of his family, the Dominicans sent him to Cologne to study under Albert the Great, one of the greatest educators of his time. Here some of his friends thought he was slow to learn and called him the "Dumb Ox." But while he may have been slow, he was sure. St. Albert recognized his great intelligence. Soon Thomas was the first scholar in his class. Not long after, he was the first scholar in Europe.

St. Thomas worked hard to explain many of the problems that are faced when trying to understand the teachings of the Church. His works are still read all around the world as a great source of truth. This should convince us that talents are worth only what use we make of them.

Church of St. Sernin, Toulouse, France

THE SITE OF THE TOMB OF ST. THOMAS AQUINAS

Tomb of St. Dominic

Bologna, Italy

L E S S O N

8

/aw/ as in law

- applaud
- auctioneer
- audible
- audience
- precaution
- author
- autograph
- auxiliary
- broad
- clause
- cough
- fought
- gnawing
- haunt
- inaugurate
- launch
- laundry
- law
- sausage
- squawk

BONUS

- watermelon

NAME

The sound **/aw/** may be spelled **aw**, **au**, **a**, **oa**, or **ou**, as in l**aw**, p**au**se, w**a**ter, br**oa**d, and c**ou**gh.

A SORT BY SPELLING

Each syllable has its own sound/spelling. Sort the words by the spelling of the **/aw/** sound.

au	
aw	
a	
oa	
ou	

B DEFINITIONS

Given below are definitions to the words found in the word list. Write the appropriate word in the space provided next to the definition.

a loud, awkward sound	1.
loud enough to be heard	2.
available to provide something extra or additional	3.
a type of large fruit having a hard rind and red juicy pulp	4.
taking care in advance	5.
a food made of ground-up pork stuffed in a casing	6.
a writer, usually of books	7.
to set in motion or send off	8.
a person's handwritten signature	9.
wide or expansive	10.
a part of a sentence; a distinct part of an article	11.
to release air from the lungs quickly and loudly	12.
struggled against another in battle	13.
chewing on or nibbling at	14.
to keep returning to or to visit often	15.
to install or establish someone in office	16.
one who sells things to those willing to pay the most	17.
clothing in need of a wash	18.
the listeners or viewers of something	19.
rule; system of rules	20.
to clap hands to demonstrate approval	21.

NAME ________________

C SENTENCES

In each sentence below, there is a blank corresponding to one of the words found in the word list. Write the missing word in the space next to the sentence.

As a ___, St. Thomas More was always honest in court.	1.
The painting was sold off by the ___ to the rich benefactor, who later gave it to St. Anne's Church.	2.
We should take adequate ___ before working with scientific equipment.	3.
The ___ of the *Narnia Chronicles* is Clive Staples Lewis, known as C. S. Lewis.	4.
The Jewish people ___ bravely in a battle against the terrorists.	5.
The baseball player's ___ was on the baseball.	6.
The speaker waited for the audience to ___ before he began his carefully prepared speech.	7.
The cowboy tipped his ___ brimmed hat as John Wayne passed by.	8.
The sound of the Rosary being said was barely ___ in the large cathedral.	9.
St. Therese developed a terrible ___ shortly before she died.	10.
Mom likes to keep a cold ___ in the refrigerator on hot days.	11.
In the morning, Father Steven liked to eat Polish ___ with his eggs.	12.
The mouse began ___ on the ropes that bound the lion in order to free him.	13.
The children helped their mother by putting the ___ in the washing machine.	14.
The falcon let out a terrific ___ as he dove to seize the mouse running across the field.	15.

D STORY TIME

Read the following story, paying attention to the underlined words. Notice how they use the spelling rule to the right.

/**aw**/ in l**aw**, p**au**se, w**a**ter, br**oa**d, c**ou**gh

St. Dominic

St. Dominic was a Spaniard who, after much thought and prayer, resolved to give his life to God. He was a man of exceptional talent and unusual holiness. He soon attracted followers. People of that time had a great need for lessons in their religion because teachers of false doctrines were deceiving many. Dominic sought good Catholic men and organized his followers into a religious order, called the Order of Preachers. The pope approved it in 1216. Dominic performed another important service for the Church by founding an order for women.

Dominic played an important role in the Church at this time. Both the laity and the clergy were ignorant of many moral and theological truths. Until this time, preaching was the concern of only the bishops. When Dominic organized his group of preachers, he taught them the catechism. He gave the Church the help she sorely needed.

Every Catholic ought to be reminded that we owe a special debt to St. Dominic because he helped spread devotion to the Mother of God through the Rosary. The Dominican order continues to promote the Rosary.

First Quarter Review

LESSON 1	LESSON 2	LESSON 3	LESSON 4
bloom	barefoot	approach	allowance
droop	bullet	cello	arouse
fireproof	bulletin	chose	bough
gloom	bullion	envelope	bounce
groove	cushion	foe	council
homeschool	driftwood	goes	counsel
ooze	fulfill	homely	crouch
proof	good-by	homemade	doubt
roof	good-bye	homogenize	drown
roost	livelihood	loaf	foul
scoop	lunar	loaves	how's
shoot	movable	mediocre	mound
smooth	pursue	motion	nowadays
stool	pursuing	noticeable	ounce
toothbrush	route	nowhere	pound
zookeeper	routine	obedience	prowl
whom	salute	old-fashioned	scout
youth	truly	omitted	scowl
youthful	tulip	oversee	shout
jewelry	tuna	prose	shower
BONUS	BONUS	BONUS	BONUS
newscast	dilute	omission	sprout

- Pronounce each word for correct spelling.
- Say the word, spell it, and say it again.
- Divide each word into syllables.
- Take an oral pretest of all these words, then spell each misspelled word three times.

LESSON 5	LESSON 6	LESSON 7	LESSON 8
appointment	acquaintance	bothered	applaud
account	acquainted	approximate	auctioneer
android	remainder	blossom	audible
boycott	ancient	chopped	audience
boysenberry	anyway	conference	precaution
compound	associate	content	author
decoy	behave	contest	autograph
denounce	behavior	cooperate	auxiliary
employ	annual	cooperation	broad
enjoyable	answered	dropped	clause
foyer	antarctic	fossil	cough
hoist	apparatus	holiday	fought
household	apt	optimism	gnawing
renown	asterisk	otter	haunt
touchdown	athletics	patriotic	inaugurate
tower	avenue	policy	launch
turquoise	bachelor	prompt	laundry
undoubtedly	bankruptcy	shock	law
warehouse	banquet	solid	sausage
whereabouts	beatitude	sovereign	squawk
BONUS	BONUS	BONUS	BONUS
discount	beatify	volume	watermelon

LESSON

10

/aw/ as in all

alter
altercation
alternative
altogether
although
asphalt
assault
bald
balsa
baseball
basketball
false
fault
haul
halt
halter
scald
somersault
stall
vault

BONUS

waltz

NAME ______________________

The sound /**aw**/ may be spelled **a**, or **au**, as in **a**ll, b**a**ld, and f**au**lt.

A SORT BY SPELLING

Each syllable has its own sound/spelling. Sort the words by the spelling of the letters **all**, **al**, and **aul**.

all	
al	
aul	

B DEFINITIONS

Given below are definitions to the words found in the word list. Write the appropriate word in the space provided next to the definition.

an option or choice	1.
a graceful ballroom dance	2.
in spite of the fact that	3.
not true; incorrect	4.
a black, tarry mixture used to pave roads	5.
a sport played with a bat and a small, hard ball	6.
to pull with effort	7.
to stop or to cause to stop	8.
sudden attack	9.
lacking a natural covering	10.
a sport in which a team tries to throw a ball through the other team's hoop	11.
disappointed, dejected	12.
a room or compartment for storage or safe-keeping	13.
to stop marching; to bring to a stop	14.
a rope or strap for leading an animal	15.
an error or flaw in something	16.
a noisy argument	17.
to burn with a hot liquid	18.
a forward flip	19.
all in all, overall	20.
a small raft	21.

NAME ____________________

C SENTENCES

In each sentence below, there is a blank corresponding to one of the words found in the word list. Write the missing word in the space next to the sentence.

Mom said it is my own ___ for not being more careful.	1.
After Jesus' miracle of the multiplication of the loaves and the fishes, there were left over ___ twelve baskets of bread.	2.
My brother and my dad love to play ___ every Sunday afternoon.	3.
The soldiers were under ___ from the enemy soldiers.	4.
Johann Strauss wrote the music of "The Blue Danube," which is the most famous ___ ever written.	5.
Paul will help Tom ___ the wagon filled with wood.	6.
Grandpa is very old, and his head is ___.	7.
The test in history was filled with true and ___ questions.	8.
___ was first developed by Dr. James Naismith to be played with a ball and a basket.	9.
The general ordered the marching soldiers to ___.	10.
At the lake, the boys tried to build a ___ with reeds.	11.
The police officer stopped an ___ between two protestors.	12.
He jumped off the vault and finished his exercise with a ___ on the floor.	13.
Jane uses a leather ___ with her horse.	14.
The tailor will ___ the length of his pants.	15.

D STORY TIME

Read the following story, paying attention to the underlined words. Notice how they use the spelling rule to the right.

/**aw**/ in **a**ll, b**a**ld, and f**au**lt

The Hundred Years' War

The Hundred Years' War was France's defense against the English assault. The English kings asserted their claim to the French throne through a French princess. The French fought to avoid an English monarchy in their country. The claims of the English king threw the country of France into a seemingly perpetual tumult from 1337 until 1453.

It was not the will of God for the English king to rule France. God had an alternate plan in mind. Through heavenly visions, a young, seemingly normal girl named Joan of Arc came to lead the French forces against the English. Joan won many astounding victories against the English, at a time in which it appeared that the English would be triumphant.

Some scoundrels, though they were French, did not like Joan. They allied themselves with the English and eventually were able to capture Joan and turn her over to the English. After an unfair trial, in which the usual rules of trial were not followed, Joan of Arc was convicted of heresy and burned at the stake in the year 1431. Despite her execution, it was Joan and the French who ultimately triumphed. Thus France remained staunchly Catholic after England became a Protestant country during the rule of Henry VIII.

After the English were finally driven out of France, Joan's case was reopened during the Pontificate of Pope Callixtus III. The retrial, which was overseen by Inquisitor-General Jean Brehal, found that Joan had been innocent of all charges brought against her. The new inquiry found great fault with Joan's earlier trial, and decided that Joan had been executed for political reasons.

Joan of Arc was canonized by Pope Benedict XV in 1920. Her feast day is May 30.

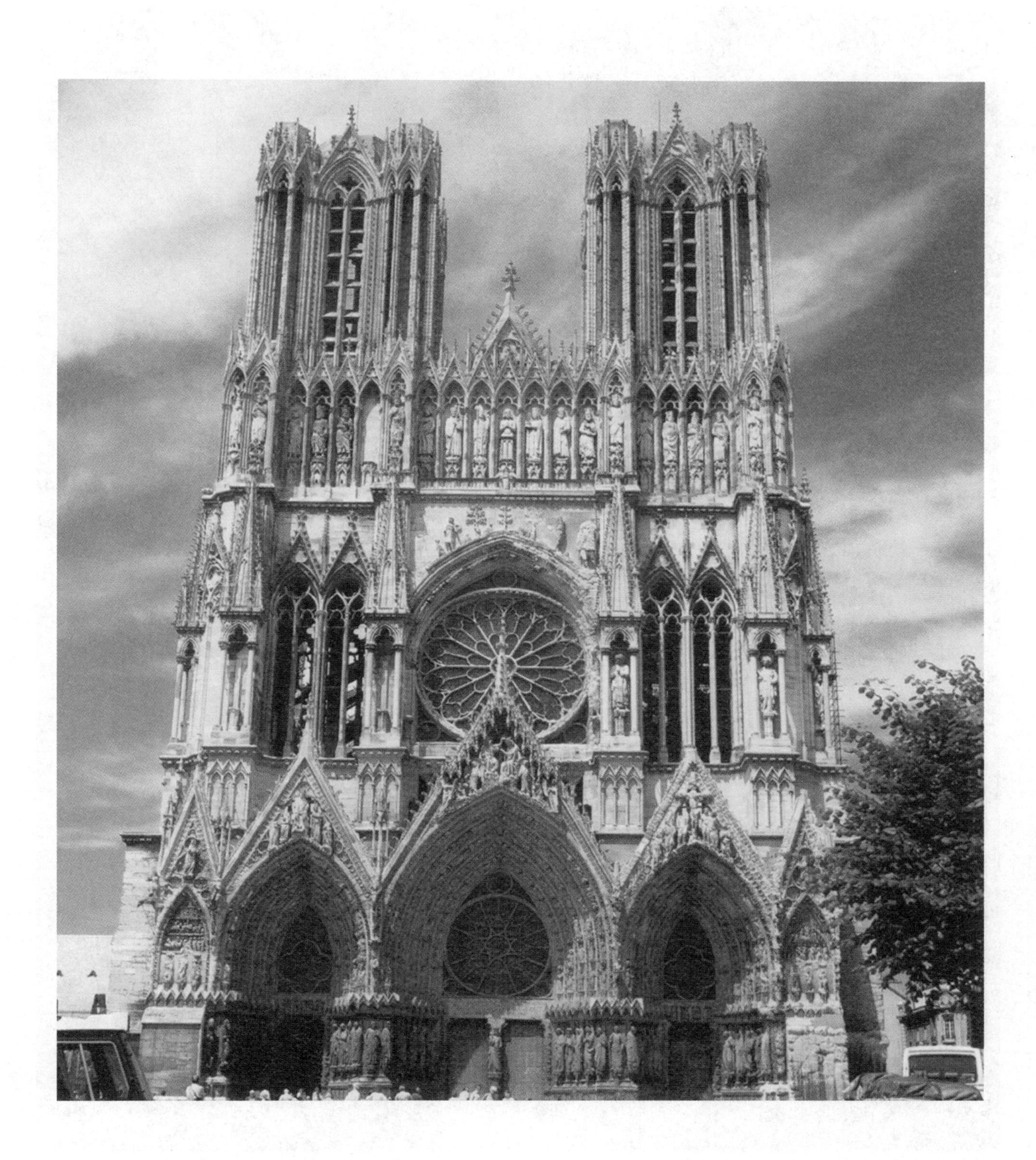

Reims Cathedral

Reims, France

St. Louis of France Renaissance Church, Rome, Italy

LESSON

11

/oh/ as in old

- anecdote
- appropriate
- erroneous
- growth
- meadow
- pillow
- potato
- potatoes
- robot
- rodeo
- shallow
- soldier
- solos
- sopranos
- sorrow
- stereos
- studios
- thorough
- cocoa
- tomorrow

BONUS

- volcanoes

NAME

The long vowel sound /**oh**/ may be spelled **o**, **oe**, **ow**, or **ough**, as in **o**ld, t**oe**s, pill**ow**, and thor**ough**.

A SORT BY SPELLING

Each syllable has its own sound/spelling. Sort the words by the spelling of the sound of /**oh**/.

o	
oe	
ow	
ough	

B DEFINITIONS

Given below are definitions to the words found in the word list. Write the appropriate word in the space provided next to the definition.

Definition	
the day after today	1.
wrong, mistaken	2.
a show of various horsemanship skills	3.
a short, often humorous story	4.
development, expansion or increase	5.
more than one potato	6.
performances in which there is only one person	7.
white vegetable, delicious mashed with gravy	8.
person in the army	9.
a machine designed to do work	10.
fissures in the earth from which magma erupts or oozes	11.
not deep	12.
suitable or proper for the situation	13.
a soft, stuffed cushion for one's head	14.
working places, usually for artists	15.
the highest voices in a choir	16.
sound systems	17.
complete; without omissions	18.
deep sadness, grief	19.
a wide, open grassy space	20.
a warm chocolate drink	21.

NAME ____________________

C SENTENCES

In each sentence below, there is a blank corresponding to one of the words found in the word list. Write the missing word in the space next to the sentence.

The ___ in the opera had amazingly high voices.	1.
A heretic is one who has ___ opinions about the truths of the Church.	2.
The river was so ___, that our canoe scraped the rocks.	3.
Father asked parents to make sure their children wore ___ clothes to church.	4.
My parents decided to build our new house in a beautiful ___ near the river.	5.
My grandpa needed a special ___ to rest his head after his surgery.	6.
Our Irish family likes ___ much more than rice or pasta.	7.
The Catholic television ___ were filled with guests when Mother Angelica appeared.	8.
My uncle certainly showed his horsemanship skills in yesterday's ___.	9.
My grandpa loves a hot cup of delicious ___ on cold evenings.	10.
In the musical recital, several homeschooling students sang ___.	11.
We were surprised at the ___ of our garden after a week of rain.	12.
My brother is proud of being a ___ so he can defend our nation against terrorists.	13.
Visitors can view some of the eruptions from the Hawaiian ___.	14.
Our family was filled with ___ after Grandmother died of cancer.	15.

D STORY TIME

Read the following story, paying attention to the underlined words. Notice how they use the spelling rule to the right.

/**oh**/ in **o**ld, t**oe**s, pill**ow**, thor**ough**

The Renaissance

Renaissance is a French word that means "rebirth." The Renaissance refers to an era in European history that followed the Middle Ages. During this time, there was a "rebirth" and growth of the learning and wisdom of the ancient Greeks and Romans which had been lost or forgotten in much of Europe. This rediscovery of ancient wisdom led to an invigoration of European culture in general.

One of the most important aspects of the Renaissance was a growth in a philosophy called "humanism," which extols and exalts the abilities and achievements of people. There is nothing inherently erroneous in such thinking, but humanist thinkers sometimes placed themselves in opposition to God. In its most extreme form, humanism can lead to the idea that human beings do not need God anymore because humans have become so godlike themselves.

Despite this tendency toward placing too much faith in mankind, the Renaissance did produce some remarkable achievements. In art, especially, the Renaissance brought about masterpieces that are admired even today. Renaissance painters began using methods of perspective and shading that gave their work a very realistic look. (Perspective means showing objects as someone standing in a certain place would see the objects. Shading means using light and shadows to give realistic lighting to objects in a painting.) Sculptors and painters, such as Leonardo da Vinci, studied human anatomy so that their works could be scientifically correct. This was in great contrast to earlier works of art, in which an artist would be more concerned that his spiritual point was clear rather than his characters perfectly formed.

The Renaissance also produced masterpieces of written work, such as plays and poems. The early Renaissance writer Petrarch is known for composing a series of hundreds of poems to a woman named "Laura." In England, the Renaissance brought about the flowering of the play, under such notable authors as William Shakespeare and Christopher Marlowe.

The idea of the Renaissance also led to a flowering of inventions, such as the printing press and the compass. Before the printing press, books had to be copied by hand, which meant that very few people could own a book. But with the advent of the printing press, many more people could have access to books of their own. The compass allowed sailors to travel farther and with more confidence because it lessened their dependence on using the stars to find their direction. Without the compass, and a related tool called a "sextant," the great voyages of discovery in the 1400's and 1500's would have been almost impossible.

LESSON

12

/ee/ as in fleet

attorney
breathe
carefree
chiefs
fleet
Greek
greet
grief
guarantee
knee
needle
nineteenth
rotary
screen
sleeve
speech
squeeze
succeed
sweetheart
weekend

BONUS

wheelchair

NAME ______________________

The long vowel sound /**ee**/ may be spelled **ee**, **ea**, **ie**, **ey**, or **y**, as in fl**ee**t, br**ea**the, ch**ie**f, attorn**ey**, and rotar**y**.

A SORT BY SPELLING

Each syllable has its own sound/spelling. Sort the words by the spelling of the /**ee**/ sound.

ee	
ea	
ie	
ey	
y	

B DEFINITIONS

Given below are definitions to the words found in the word list. Write the appropriate word in the space provided next to the definition.

Definition	
great sorrow or heartache	1.
lighthearted, happy-go-lucky	2.
lawyer	3.
a very kind or delightful person; a beloved	4.
leaders	5.
the part of a shirt or jacket that encloses the arm	6.
to welcome; to address kindly	7.
to win or achieve something	8.
to promise or pledge something	9.
language, talking	10.
the region in the middle part of the leg	11.
a small, sharp-pointed object used for sewing	12.
to pinch or compress something	13.
a chair equipped with wheels, used for handicapped people	14.
to inhale and exhale	15.
revolving	16.
a barrier or mesh for a window	17.
a large group of vehicles, usually ships	18.
from Greece	19.
pertaining to the number nineteen	20.
the end of the week, including Sunday	21.

NAME ____________________

C SENTENCES

In each sentence below, there is a blank corresponding to one of the words found in the word list. Write the missing word in the space next to the sentence.

My grandfather must use a ___ to get around since the operation on his leg.	1.
Dad loves to order a ___ salad with black olives, peppers, and tomatoes.	2.
With ___ and thread, Mom quickly sewed the torn shirt.	3.
Mom thought little Tommy should go to ___ class because of his stutter.	4.
The bride and groom stood at the door to ___ the guests after the Nuptial Mass.	5.
Our parish is having a special retreat this ___.	6.
Little Johnny genuflected on his ___ in front of the Blessed Sacrament.	7.
The ___ for the pro-life demonstrators pleaded their case in court yesterday.	8.
During the ___ century, two popular children's books were *Little Women* and *Tom Sawyer*.	9.
Dad was very unhappy when Bobby broke the ___ door!	10.
The three babies were ___ as they played together in the playpen.	11.
The tiny newborn baby began to ___ on her own immediately.	12.
When my brothers were wrestling on the floor, David's ___ was torn off his shirt!	13.
Father George could not ___ that he would be at the meeting on time.	14.
We cannot expect to ___ in our studies if we are not praying daily for help.	15.

D STORY TIME

Read the following story, paying attention to the underlined words. Notice how they use the spelling rule to the right.

/**ee**/ in fl**ee**t, br**ea**the, ch**ie**f, attorn**ey**, rotar**y**

Protestant Revolt

Toward the end of the Renaissance, the Catholic Church was faced with religious revolts in many European countries. This period is usually referred to as the Protestant Reformation. However, the result was more of a revolt than a reformation.

Martin Luther was the first major leader of the Reformation. Luther was born in Germany in 1483. He studied law, but decided to become a monk and a professor at the University of Wittenburg in Germany. As a monk, Luther became conscious of the abuses that were occurring in the Church. These practices were not approved by the Church, and Luther had a right to criticize them. However, he soon denied some of the chief teachings of the Church. He began to teach that man could be saved through faith alone. The Catholic Church always taught that each person must express his faith by performing good deeds.

The Church has always urged the faithful to receive the sacraments in order to obtain sanctifying grace. Luther believed that faith alone was necessary; he rejected five of the sacraments and the need for sanctifying grace. He believed that each person could decide the meaning of the Bible for himself. His teaching led many people to start their own religion.

The term *Protestant* came to be applied to all those who broke away from the Catholic Church. Although the different Protestant groups did not always agree with one another on religious doctrine, they all rejected the Catholic Church as the teacher of the truths of Christianity. Pope Paul III in 1545 called together cardinals and bishops who started the Catholic Reformation. A major result was a re-conversion of Protestants through a renewal of the truths of the Faith which resulted in a new zeal for the Faith.

ALL SAINTS' CHURCH IN WITTENBERG, GERMANY

THE CHURCH WHERE LUTHER STARTED THE PROTESTANT REVOLT

THE CATHEDRAL OF NOTRE DAME IN PARIS, FRANCE

A SYMBOL OF FRENCH NATIONALISM AS WELL AS AN IMPORTANT CATHOLIC CHURCH

NOTE THE FLAGS ATOP THE TOWERS.

LESSON

13

/eh/ as in accept

- acceptable
- dedicate
- accessory
- breath
- correct
- dwell
- elevator
- misspelled
- protective
- aggressive
- amendment
- ascend
- assemble
- begged
- collect
- debt
- delegate
- dentist
- effective
- exception

BONUS

- depend

NAME ____________________

The short vowel sound **/eh/** may be spelled **e** or **ea**, as in acc**e**pt and br**ea**th.

A SORT BY SYLLABLES

Each syllable has its own sound/spelling. Sort the words by the number of syllables.

1	
2	
3	
4	

B DEFINITIONS

Given below are definitions to the words found in the word list. Write the appropriate word in the space provided next to the definition.

to set apart for a purpose	1.
satisfactory, adequate	2.
to rely on someone else	3.
something that comes along with something else	4.
hostile or overly assertive	5.
spelled incorrectly	6.
to live in a place	7.
a case where a rule does not apply	8.
a doctor who specializes in treating teeth	9.
the air taken into the body by inhaling or out by exhaling	10.
a representative for another person	11.
producing a desired effect	12.
accurate; proper and acceptable	13.
intended to keep something safe from harm	14.
to rise	15.
a movable cage designed to move people between floors of a building	16.
to put together	17.
pleaded for something	18.
to gather something	19.
an adjustment or change, especially in a law	20.
an obligation to pay someone	21.

NAME ______________________________

C SENTENCES

In each sentence below, there is a blank corresponding to one of the words found in the word list. Write the missing word in the space next to the sentence.

My sister has decided to ___ her life to helping the poor.	1.
Mother praised the children for their ___ behavior at the wedding Mass.	2.
My ___ wants to check my teeth every six months.	3.
Our parish is trying to ___ food and clothes to help the family whose house burned down.	4.
Most Indians liked to ___ in a tent so they could move often.	5.
Father Bill said that the boys' naughty behavior was not ___.	6.
We must try our best to pay off any ___ we owe to others.	7.
Mother said I need to write my ___ words five times!	8.
Oliver developed special bullet-proof ___ vests for policemen.	9.
Mother Teresa ___ for food and clothes for the poor people in India.	10.
Peggy likes to operate the ___ in the office building because she enjoys meeting people.	11.
Jesus' apostles crowded around Him as He began to ___ into the clouds.	12.
After working in the cellar all day, Jeanne was glad to get a ___ of fresh air.	13.
Deacon Steve is the ___ for our parish at the meeting.	14.
Many old people in that nursing home ___ on the care and nursing provided by the Sisters of St. Cecilia.	15.

D STORY TIME

Read the following story, paying attention to the underlined words. Notice how they use the spelling rule to the right.

/**eh**/ in acc**e**pt, br**ea**th

The Church and Nationalism

The Catholic Church has always been a universal Church. In fact, the word "Catholic" means universal. It has never been a church meant for only one nation or one group of people, as some churches are. According to the Catholic Church, based on the teachings of Jesus, all people are "chosen" by God since all people are called to Jesus Christ and His Church.

Catholics should look to the Church for guidance in deciding what is right and what is wrong. Some rulers of nations have opposed the Church, especially rulers who want their citizens to look only to them for guidance and rules.

The Catholic Church has always taught that a good Catholic is a good citizen since a good Catholic obeys the laws of his country, as long as these laws do not oppose the teachings of the Church. The Catholic recognizes that the authority of a ruler comes from God, but a ruler must follow God's laws to protect the citizens and allow them to worship God first.

Some rulers do not like being judged by Church authorities. The idea that a person's loyalty is primarily to his nation rather than to God or God's Church is called "nationalism."

Nationalism is thought to have good and bad qualities. There is nothing wrong for people to believe they are part of a nation that is working toward the common good. The development of a nation has often ended local conflicts between ethnic groups, tribes, or families. However, nationalism sometimes leads people to support the actions of their country even when their country is doing wrong, such as Germany in World War II.

The proper attitude of the Christian should be like that of St. Thomas More who said in 1535 to the English people and to King Henry VIII that he was "the king's good servant but God's first."

LESSON

14

/yoo/ as in use, /uh/ as in ugly

Eucharist
usury
flood
govern
governor
grandmother
lovable
lovely
loving
onion
rough
shove
shovel
shoveling
somebody
sometime
touched
touch
ugly
usable

BONUS

using

NAME ____________________

The long vowel sound **/yoo/** may be spelled **u** or **eu**, as in **u**se and **Eu**charist. The short vowel sound **/uh/** may be spelled **u**, **oo**, **o**, or **ou**, as in **u**gly, fl**oo**d, l**o**ve, and t**ou**ch.

A SORT BY VOWEL SOUND

Each syllable has its own sound/spelling. Sort the words by the sound of **u** in **use**, and the sound of **u** in **ugly**.

use	
ugly	

B DEFINITIONS

Given below are definitions to the words found in the word list. Write the appropriate word in the space provided next to the definition.

charging too much interest on a loan	1.
lifting and throwing with a shovel	2.
a great overflow of water onto the land	3.
to rule over	4.
a person whose identity is not known	5.
able to be used	6.
caring, tender	7.
a person who rules over others	8.
a popular vegetable for seasoning foods, such as hamburgers	9.
the mother of a person's mother or father	10.
able to be easily loved	11.
putting something to use	12.
delicately beautiful	13.
not smooth, uneven	14.
an unspecified time	15.
to feel or handle	16.
unattractive	17.
Christ's Body, Blood, Soul and Divinity under the appearances of bread and wine	18.
to push violently	19.
having made contact with or handled in the past	20.
a tool used for digging	21.

NAME ________________________________

C SENTENCES

In each sentence below, there is a blank corresponding to one of the words found in the word list. Write the missing word in the space next to the sentence.

People were warned not to do heavy ___ during the snowstorm.	1. ____________
The candidate said that he would ___ his city with respect for all the people.	2. ____________
The pro-life ___ worked hard to sign good pro-life legislation.	3. ____________
We are not allowed to ___ the holy relic of the true Cross, but we may kiss it.	4. ____________
Dad said to charge that much interest on a loan is called ___ .	5. ____________
My dad broke the ___ when he was digging in the rose garden.	6. ____________
Our pastor said we should try to attend Mass and receive Jesus in the Holy ___ every First Friday.	7. ____________
The nuns at the hospital were ___ and caring toward the patients.	8. ____________
Mom did not want to see us ___ the sharp knives in the kitchen.	9. ____________
God told Noah there would be a great ___ that would cover all the earth.	10. ____________
My sister made her own wedding gown, which was especially ___ because of the tiny white pearls.	11. ____________
Dad likes the strong flavor of ___ in almost all his food!	12. ____________
Because the road was in disrepair, it was a ___ ride for my grandma.	13. ____________
People were cured of their diseases when they simply ___ the hem of the cloak of Jesus.	14. ____________
Sister Mary warned the boys not to ___ each other on the playground.	15. ____________

D STORY TIME

Read the following story, paying attention to the underlined words. Notice how they use the spelling rule to the right.

/**yoo**/ in **u**se, **Eu**charist
/**uh**/ in **u**gly, fl**oo**d, l**o**ve, t**ou**ch

The Babylonian Captivity

Pope Benedict XI (1303-1304) was a strong-willed pope who did not give in to France. This caused political problems in Europe. When he died, the College of Cardinals elected a man of opposite tendencies to govern the Church. This man was Pope Clement V, a French citizen.

When Pope Clement V was elected, instead of going to Rome, he moved the papacy to Avignon, France. Other popes followed his example and remained in Avignon. For a brief intermission, Pope Urban V moved back to the Vatican, but the French king persuaded him to return to France. This time is called the Babylonian captivity because, like the Jews, the Church was removed from her true home.

Finally, the passionate and loving pleas of Saint Catherine of Siena convinced Pope Gregory XI to return his pontificate to Rome. The Babylonian captivity was finally over, and the spirit of loyalty to Rome was reinforced.

Let us remember to try to receive Jesus Christ every day in the sacrament of the Holy Eucharist, and to include the pope in our daily prayers. We can expect extra graces from Our Lord if we remember to include His earthly vicar in our prayers.

Avignon Cathedral

Avignon, France

Canterbury Cathedral

London, England

NAME

LESSON 15

/iy/ as in ice /ih/ as in it

analyze
considerable
considerate
consistent
grandchild
hygiene
iceberg
ignore
strict
strictly
type
arrived
assist
assistance
beginning
billboard
biscuit
brittle
clientele
continue

BONUS

continued

The long vowel sound /**iy**/ may be spelled **i** or **y**, as in **i**ce and t**y**pe.
The short vowel sound /**ih**/ may be spelled **i**, as in **i**t.

A SORT BY VOWEL SOUND

Each syllable has its own sound/spelling. Sort the words by the sound of /i/ in **ice**, and the sound of **i** in **it**.

ice	
it	

B DEFINITIONS

Given below are definitions to the words found in the word list. Write the appropriate word in the space provided next to the definition.

to pay no attention	1.
to closely examine something	2.
unchanging in behavior	3.
support or aid	4.
easily broken or cracked	5.
did the same thing without stopping	6.
a type of bread roll	7.
a large floating mass of ice	8.
to aid or help	9.
carefully enforcing rules; permitting no exceptions	10.
in a strict manner; carefully obeying rules	11.
significant; important; large in extent or degree	12.
a kind of something	13.
the child of a person's child	14.
to keep on doing something	15.
reached or came to a destination	16.
thoughtful; caring about the needs of others	17.
the start of something	18.
a large flat surface to display outdoor advertisements	19.
personal care; cleanliness	20.
the customers or patrons of a business	21.

NAME ____________________

C SENTENCES

In each sentence below, there is a blank corresponding to one of the words found in the word list. Write the missing word in the space next to the sentence.

The rescue workers ___ throughout the day to help people struggling in the flood waters caused by Hurricane Katrina.	1.
The missionary nuns gave ___ to the sick as well as the dying.	2.
My mom is very ___ about our doing the math and English assignments every day.	3.
Several donors gave a ___ amount of money to St. James Church.	4.
Mother Teresa of Calcutta trained her nuns to ___ the poorest of the poor.	5.
The Catholic senator is ___ in voting for pro-life legislation.	6.
When the Titanic hit the tip of an ___, no one realized the enormity of the consequences.	7.
Success for students means to ___ in doing each assignment until it is finished.	8.
It is foolish to ___ a math assignment because it may be essential for the next lesson.	9.
The doctor said he must ___ the x-rays to find where the bone is broken.	10.
When the pope ___ in St. Peter's Square in the pope-mobile, the whole crowd began to clap and sing.	11.
The young pianist started playing the ___ of a Mozart piano concerto.	12.
The missionary in Jamaica was very sensitive and ___ in dealing with the young people.	13.
Nothing is better than a homemade ___, fresh out of Grandma's oven!	14.
On the drive home, we saw a pro-life ___.	15.

D STORY TIME

Read the following story, paying attention to the underlined words. Notice how they use the spelling rule to the right.

/**iy**/ in **i**ce and t**y**pe
/**ih**/ in **i**t

Mary Tudor

After Henry VIII formed the Anglican Church in England in 1534, Catholics suffered for their religious beliefs. Any Catholic who would not recognize Henry as the ultimate spiritual authority was considered a traitor. Henry went even further, however, by persecuting the Church. One of the saddest parts of this persecution was the abolition of all monasteries in England. For hundreds of years, monasteries had been centers of learning in England, but King Henry decided that he could raise money for his government by seizing the monasteries and selling off their goods and their lands.

After the death of Henry VIII in 1547, Henry's very young son, Edward VI, became king. During his reign, England became ever more Protestant. During this time, the Mass was forbidden in England and many churches were pillaged and destroyed. Edward's reign was short. He died of tuberculosis at the age of 15.

The next person in line for the throne was Mary Tudor. Unlike Edward, she had been raised a Catholic and remained firm in that belief. Soon after she became queen, Mary took steps to reconcile England to the Church. However, she proved herself a rather unwise ruler. She executed a large number of Protestants, including several bishops. Even worse for her rule, Mary decided to wed King Philip II of Spain. The people of England did not like the idea of having a Spanish king. This turned the people against her.

Like her brother Edward, Mary lived and reigned only a short time. She died of cancer in November of 1558 at the age of 42. Mary was succeeded on the throne by her half-sister Elizabeth. When Elizabeth became queen, she promised to uphold the Catholic Faith. However, she did not keep her promise for long.

LESSON

16

/k/ as in kite

ache
architect
calendar
campaign
campus
cancel
canceled
cancellation
canvas
canvass
capable
catering
character
Christian
echoes
firecracker
headache
khaki
nickel
scholastic

BONUS

technique

NAME ______________________

The sound /**k**/ may be spelled **k**, **c**, **ck**, or **ch**, as in **k**ite, **c**anvas, ni**ck**el, and e**ch**o.

A SORT BY SPELLING

Each syllable has its own sound/spelling. Sort the words by the spelling of the sound of /k/.

k	
c	
ck	
ch	

B DEFINITIONS

Given below are definitions to the words found in the word list. Write the appropriate word in the space provided next to the definition.

a person who designs buildings	1.
a type of heavy, coarse fabric	2.
having to do with scholars and school	3.
the five-cent coin of American currency	4.
a person in a book, movie, or play	5.
a series of military or political operations	6.
to go through an area to ask people for votes	7.
reflections of sound; reverberations	8.
a school's buildings and the surrounding property	9.
to call something off or to remove	10.
called off; deleted; removed completely	11.
a way of going about something; a procedure	12.
the act of canceling something	13.
a dull pain	14.
a tan or sand-colored fabric	15.
a lingering pain in the head	16.
an arrangement of time into days, weeks, and months	17.
competent; able to do something	18.
food preparation for someone else, usually by a company	19.
a follower of Christ	20.
a small explosive designed to make noise	21.

NAME ______________________________

C SENTENCES

In each sentence below, there is a blank corresponding to one of the words found in the word list. Write the missing word in the space next to the sentence.

Father Burns ___ the teen retreat because of the bad weather.	1.
My aunt said she would be in charge of the music and ___ for my sister's wedding reception.	2.
The ___ who designed St. Matthew's cathedral came to the grand opening.	3.
St. Mark's Church published a beautiful religious ___ for the new year.	4.
Though Timmy is very young, Father Long said he is a very ___ altar boy.	5.
The main ___ in the story I read is St. Anthony, the miracle worker.	6.
Jenny attends a Catholic college which has the Stations of the Cross on the college ___.	7.
I had to ___ my appointment so that I could attend the Rosary novena.	8.
Dad said that if the ___ in my tooth continues, he will take me to the dentist.	9.
The ___ of the Spelling Bee caused great unhappiness among those who had studied so hard!	10.
To be a ___ in the early Church meant persecution and possibly martyrdom.	11.
My beautiful forest-green ___ camping tent has a mesh rear window!	12.
Though the missionary priest had a ___ himself, he continued to visit the sick.	13.
Our pro-life state delegate asked for money for his re-election ___.	14.
Our pro-life state delegate asked that we ___ our neighborhood to see what kind of support he has for his re-election.	15.

D STORY TIME

Read the following story, paying attention to the underlined words. Notice how they use the spelling rule to the right.

/**k**/ in **k**ite, **c**anvas, ni**ck**el, e**ch**o

The Mother of God

The Blessed Virgin Mary is the Mother of God, Christ the King. She was the instrument by which God gave to us the gift of Heaven. She was chosen to be God's Mother because she was very holy and loved God very much. God gave her abundant graces, including keeping her free from original sin.

When Christ was on earth, Mary cared for Him and loved Him above all things. Though He was her Son, she was obedient to Him, following His teaching and striving to do His Will.

As His Mother, Mary is closer to Him than we are. Mary wants us to join her and her Son in Heaven. If we ask her to help us, she will in turn ask her Son to give us the graces that we need to get to Heaven.

The role of the Blessed Mother in asking Jesus to help others is seen in the story of the marriage feast at Cana. While they were at the wedding feast, Mary came to Jesus and told Him that the wedding party was running out of wine. When Mary communicated this need to Jesus, He asked the servants to bring large jars of water. When the water was brought to Jesus, He changed the water into wine. When the new wine was given to the chief butler at the party, who did not know where the wine came from, he said to the bridegroom, "Most people serve the best wine first, but you have kept the best wine until the end."

At the wedding party, Mary directed the servants to "Do whatever He tells you." This is the message that Mary always brings to Christians. Mary is like a sure compass, always pointing us to Jesus, and telling us, "Do whatever He tells you."

LESSON

17

/f/ as in forget

affection
affiliate
apostrophe
dolphin
forbid
forceful
forcible
forehead
foreign
forget
forgetting
forgiveness
fortunate
orphan
pamphlet
phase
philosophy
rough
therefore
tough

BONUS

zephyr

NAME ______________________

The sound **/f/** may be spelled **f**, **ff**, **ph**, or **gh**, as in **f**orget, a**ff**ect, dol**ph**in, and rou**gh**.

A SORT BY SPELLING

Each syllable has its own sound/spelling. Sort the words by the spelling of the sound of /**f**/.

f	
ff	
ph	
gh	

B DEFINITIONS

Given below are definitions to the words found in the word list. Write the appropriate word in the space provided next to the definition.

a gentle or light breeze	1.
an associate or partner	2.
a type of sea-dwelling mammal	3.
not gentle; very powerful	4.
not smooth; uneven	5.
done by force or violence	6.
pardon or absolution from blame	7.
sturdy, hardy	8.
a strong display of fondness or liking	9.
to fail to remember; not to recall	10.
the study of and search for wisdom	11.
from a different country; unknown or unfamiliar	12.
not remembering; failing to recall	13.
having unexpected good things happen	14.
a punctuation mark used in contractions	15.
the top of the face; the front of the head	16.
a child whose parents have died	17.
and so; thus	18.
a short piece of literature written to promote something	19.
a stage or part of a longer process	20.
to prohibit or to tell someone not to do something	21.

NAME ____________________

C SENTENCES

In each sentence below, there is a blank corresponding to one of the words found in the word list. Write the missing word in the space next to the sentence.

We should never give up asking Jesus for ___ for our sins.	1.
My father said he overcooked the meat and it was too ___ to chew!	2.
I do not like contractions because I do not like to use an ___.	3.
The burglar obviously made a ___ entry because the door was broken off the hinges.	4.
The Ten Commandments ___ us to offend God and to offend our neighbors.	5.
With the rain coming down, the pastor said, "___, we shall proceed to have our picnic in the gym!"	6.
Mom says my two-year-old brother is going through a yelling ___.	7.
The general was a ___ speaker who encouraged his soldiers to fight bravely.	8.
My driveway is too ___ to skate on so we went to the church parking lot.	9.
The young twins would often walk arm in arm, obviously showing their ___ for each other.	10.
Father poured the water over the ___ of the tiny baby as she was baptized.	11.
A young Russian ___ was adopted by Mrs. Murray.	12.
That large family was ___ because their grandfather gave them his huge house as a gift.	13.
Most high schools require students to study two years of a ___ language.	14.
The candidate handed out a ___ to voters in his district to explain his views.	15.

D STORY TIME

Read the following story, paying attention to the underlined words. Notice how they use the spelling rule to the right.

/**f**/ as in **f**orget, a**ff**ect, dol**ph**in, and rou**gh**

Queen Elizabeth I

Queen Elizabeth I of England succeeded Mary Tudor in 1558. Though she promised to reign as a Catholic, she converted to Protestantism and fashioned herself the head of the Anglican Church. This was probably as much for political reasons as for any belief she had in the Protestant faith. After Henry VIII had divorced Catherine of Aragon, he had married a woman named Anne Boleyn. Anne Boleyn was the mother of Elizabeth. The marriage to Anne Boleyn, however, had been a false marriage not recognized by the Catholic Church. Since Elizabeth was not born of a true marriage, her claim to be queen was suspect. However, if she rejected the Catholic Faith, then she could also reject the teachings of the Church regarding marriage, and therefore claim that she was born of a legal marriage.

With the cooperation of her aides, she returned England to Protestantism. Because no Catholic seminaries were allowed to operate in England, priests were trained in France, especially at the University of Douai. Once the priests were trained in France, they were sent to England. Priests were forced to hide in secret rooms and attics to bring the sacraments to the people. Of the priests trained in Douai, more than 160 were eventually martyred for the Faith. Some of the lay people who hid the priests were also martyred.

Despite the difficulties in practicing their Faith and the intolerance they suffered, the Catholics remained steadfast in their beliefs.

Catholics in Spain were also victims of Elizabeth's anti-Catholic reign. She encouraged English pirates to rob Spanish ships carrying the gold that was to pay for their army and for other government spending. Elizabeth even knighted Francis Drake, who spent his time raiding Catholic towns on the South American coast.

LESSON 18

Second Quarter Review

LESSON 10	LESSON 11	LESSON 12	LESSON 13
alter	anecdote	attorney	acceptable
altercation	appropriate	breathe	dedicate
alternative	erroneous	carefree	accessory
altogether	growth	chiefs	breath
although	meadow	fleet	correct
asphalt	pillow	Greek	dwell
assault	potato	greet	elevator
bald	potatoes	grief	misspelled
balsa	robot	guarantee	protective
baseball	rodeo	knee	aggressive
basketball	shallow	needle	amendment
false	soldier	nineteenth	ascend
fault	solos	rotary	assemble
haul	sopranos	screen	begged
halt	sorrow	sleeve	collect
halter	stereos	speech	debt
scald	studios	squeeze	delegate
somersault	thorough	succeed	dentist
stall	cocoa	sweetheart	effective
vault	tomorrow	weekend	exception
BONUS	BONUS	BONUS	BONUS
waltz	volcanoes	wheelchair	depend

- Pronounce each word for correct spelling.
- Say the word, spell it, and say it again.
- Divide each word into syllables.
- Take an oral pretest of all these words, then spell each misspelled word three times.

LESSON 14	LESSON 15	LESSON 16	LESSON 17
Eucharist	analyze	ache	affection
usury	considerable	architect	affiliate
flood	considerate	calendar	apostrophe
govern	consistent	campaign	dolphin
governor	grandchild	campus	forbid
grandmother	hygiene	cancel	forceful
lovable	iceberg	canceled	forcible
lovely	ignore	cancellation	forehead
loving	strict	canvas	foreign
onion	strictly	canvass	forget
rough	type	capable	forgetting
shove	arrived	catering	forgiveness
shovel	assist	character	fortunate
shoveling	assistance	Christian	orphan
somebody	beginning	echoes	pamphlet
sometime	billboard	firecracker	phase
touched	biscuit	headache	philosophy
touch	brittle	khaki	rough
ugly	clientele	nickel	therefore
usable	continue	scholastic	tough
BONUS	BONUS	BONUS	BONUS
using	continued	technique	zephyr

NAME ______________________________

LESSON 19

/sh/ as in shut

attraction
brochure
chef
Confession
construction
contribution
satisfaction
prescription
efficient
fascination
glacier
graduation
impression
opposition
partial
pollution
possession
potential
precious
profession

BONUS

ratios

The sound /**sh**/ may be spelled **sh**, **ch**, **ti**, **si**, or **ci**, as in **sh**ut, **ch**ef, attrac**ti**on, impres**si**on, and effi**ci**ent.

A SORT BY SPELLING

Each syllable has its own sound/spelling. Sort the words by the letters that spell the /**sh**/ sound.

ch	
ti	
si	
ci	

B DEFINITIONS

Given below are definitions to the words found in the word list. Write the appropriate word in the space provided next to the definition.

having the ability to happen in the future; possible	1.
a booklet or pamphlet	2.
an occupation requiring advanced education, such as doctor or lawyer	3.
process of building or putting together	4.
producing results without waste	5.
the sum of something given away; something given	6.
a relationship between two things; proportions	7.
the act of possessing or owning	8.
something that catches the attention	9.
the quality and state of being satisfied	10.
a medicine that a doctor tells a person to take	11.
a professional cook	12.
a very large body of ice moving slowly	13.
very valuable, treasured	14.
a ceremony in which students receive a diploma	15.
strong impact or effect on someone	16.
a very high degree of interest; a great attraction	17.
the action of resisting; resistance	18.
incomplete, limited	19.
the confessing of sins to a priest	20.
the act of ruining, polluting, or spoiling	21.

NAME ____________________

C SENTENCES

In each sentence below, there is a blank corresponding to one of the words found in the word list. Write the missing word in the space next to the sentence.

Jimmy's brothers had a great ___ with his new computer game.	1.
My uncle is a ___ in the little Italian restaurant in town.	2.
We should be concerned about others rather than about the ___ of goods.	3.
Our pastor asked everyone to make a larger ___ to the church to pay for the new chapel.	4.
Father Borth said we should be going to ___ at least once a month.	5.
The local ___ company is building many houses in our neighborhood.	6.
My mother gave me a very ___ gift, a relic of St. Alphonsus.	7.
The doctor gave my grandma a ___ for her headache.	8.
The high school homeschoolers scheduled a ___ ceremony after the First Friday Mass.	9.
The stirring homily Father Steven gave this morning made a strong ___ on everyone.	10.
The missionary brothers published a ___ about St. Francis.	11.
I learned that a ___ is like a great river of ice that sculpts valleys out of mountains.	12.
The town council encourages us to solve the problem of ___ by disposing of our garbage properly.	13.
The main ___ at the shrine is the relic of St. Anthony.	14.
My brother, a doctor, says the medical ___ is very rewarding.	15.

D STORY TIME

Read the following story, paying attention to the underlined words. Notice how they use the spelling rule to the right.

/**sh**/ in **sh**ut, **ch**ef, attrac**ti**on, impres**si**on, effi**ci**ent

Ireland

The attention of the Church was first shifted to Ireland when St. Patrick traveled by ship to the island around 425. Patrick had previously been taken to Ireland as a slave. Before his slavery, Patrick had not been a religious person, but during his slavery, he came to a new relationship with God. After some time in Ireland, Patrick managed to escape from his captors.

However, despite his enslavement, Patrick could not shed his love for the Irish people. He returned to them as a missionary in an attempt to bring the Catholic Faith to the Irish. His efforts had some success, but he was always expecting to be killed or enslaved again.

Patrick took bold steps to show the people that the Catholic Faith is the true Faith. At that time in Ireland, there was a custom that all the fires should be extinguished on a certain night. Then the pagan king would light a new fire to symbolize the rebirth of spring. Patrick, however, lit his own large fire as a rival to the pagan fire. It is said that Patrick's fire could not be extinguished.

Patrick was beloved by the people of Ireland for other reasons. Patrick banished all snakes from Ireland. When Patrick was explaining the Trinity to the Irish people, he used the three-leafed shamrock as an example. The shamrock is now regarded as the symbol of Ireland.

When the Protestant Revolt affected much of Europe, Ireland remained Catholic. Under Henry VIII and Elizabeth I, England conquered and ruled Ireland. Because the English were Protestant and the Irish were Catholic, the English treated the Irish very harshly. Over many centuries, English rule led to great hardship and misery for the Irish. Even to this day, the English continue to rule a section of Ireland. Despite all the efforts of the English, Ireland has retained the Catholic Faith.

LESSON

20

/s/ as in sent

accede
accelerate
anticipated
Celsius
cemetery
census
civilize
concede
conceit
conceivable
crevice
criticism
criticize
dominance
fallacy
masterpiece
percentage
performance
psychology
replacement

BONUS

violence

NAME ______________________

The sound /**s**/ may be spelled **s**, **c**, or **ps**, as in **s**ent, **c**ivilize, and **ps**ychology.

A SORT BY SPELLING

Each syllable has its own sound/spelling. Sort the words by the spelling of the /**s**/ sound.

c	
c / s	
ps	

B DEFINITIONS

Given below are definitions to the words found in the word list. Write the appropriate word in the space provided next to the definition.

expected	1.
able to be thought of; imaginable	2.
a wonderful piece of art	3.
a presentation or act	4.
a system for measuring temperature	5.
a place where dead people are buried	6.
to agree to	7.
a part or percent of something	8.
the study of the human mind and behavior	9.
to bring to an advanced state of social development	10.
too much pride in one's own worth	11.
the use of force in a way that is hurtful to others	12.
to increase speed	13.
to accept or agree to a point of debate	14.
something that takes the place of something else	15.
the act of finding fault, of criticizing	16.
an official count of all the residents of a place	17.
the act of being dominant, of controlling	18.
a false or mistaken idea	19.
to express disapproval of	20.
a deep crack or fissure	21.

NAME ______________________

C SENTENCES

In each sentence below, there is a blank corresponding to one of the words found in the word list. Write the missing word in the space next to the sentence.

We should not resort to ___ but settle matters peaceably.	1.
Do not ___ others unless you yourself are willing to accept criticism.	2.
Thirty-two degrees Fahrenheit is the same as zero degrees ___.	3.
What ___ of your income do you give to the poor?	4.
Joseph and Mary traveled to Bethlehem because the emperor wanted to take a ___.	5.
It is ___ that we will have snow on Thanksgiving Day.	6.
Please do not ___ too fast on your bicycle!	7.
I found the little kitten stuck in a ___ in the rock.	8.
At the time of Christ, most of the world was under the ___ of the Roman Empire.	9.
He ___ where I was going and got there before me.	10.
Michelangelo's famous sculpture, *Pieta*, is a great ___.	11.
It is an old custom to go to the ___ to pray for the dead on All Souls' Day.	12.
Maria heard a beautiful musical ___ at Easter time.	13.
When Jane lost her rosary, her mother gave her a ___.	14.
The debater had to ___ the point made by his opponent.	15.

D STORY TIME

Read the following story, paying attention to the underlined words. Notice how they use the spelling rule to the right.

/**s**/ in **s**ent, **c**ivilize, and **ps**ychology

Prince Henry the Navigator

Prince Henry grew up in Portugal in the fifteenth century. As a soldier fighting the Moors in north Africa, he became interested in exploration of the continent of Africa. With the inspiration and direction from Henry, Portuguese ships surveyed the coast of Africa. During Henry's reign, Portuguese ships sailed farther and farther south around the African continent. Henry directed that maps be made to guide the sailors.

Unfortunately, much of the exploration of Africa was done in order to secure slaves for use in Portugal and for sale elsewhere. Henry justified the slave trade by saying that he was converting the slaves to Christianity. The slave trade from Africa is one of the saddest chapters in the history of both Africa and Europe. Over the centuries, several million Africans were made slaves and pressed into service around the world, including in America.

Henry's work of exploration continued even after his death in 1463. In 1488, Bartholomew Diaz was the first man to sail around the Cape of Good Hope, at the southernmost point of Africa. He did not realize his accomplishment at the time. His ship was caught in a storm, and Diaz tried sailing in three directions before he was able to find land. He found himself in the Indian Ocean. Later, Vasco da Gama sailed around the Cape and brought back many treasures. Thus, Portugal's explorers were the first to find a water route to the East. In 1522, a Portuguese expedition, led by Ferdinand Magellan, became the first expedition to circumnavigate the globe.

The Portuguese explorations also established Portuguese settlements and colonies around the world. The largest and most important colony of Portugal was Brazil, in South America. Brazil has the largest number of Catholic citizens of any country in the world. Brazil gained independence from Portugal in 1822.

LESSON

21

/j/ as in jump

agent
allege
budget
college
courage
damaged
garage
genuine
gesture
gigantic
giraffe
gorgeous
image
knowledge
ledger
mileage
mortgage
privilege
sergeant
surgeon

BONUS

usage

NAME ____________________

The sound /**j**/ may be spelled **j**, **g**, or **dge**, as in **j**ump, a**g**ent, and knowle**dge**.

A SORT BY SYLLABLES

Each syllable has its own sound/spelling. Identify the syllables in each word. Sort the words by the number of syllables.

2	
3	

B DEFINITIONS

Given below are definitions to the words found in the word list. Write the appropriate word in the space provided next to the definition.

a place of higher learning	1.
a picture of something	2.
a doctor who specializes in operations	3.
someone or something that is the cause of something else	4.
bravery or strength in times of danger	5.
broken or hurt in some way	6.
real, authentic	7.
a movement of the hand	8.
the amount of money allotted for a project	9.
a building where vehicles are kept	10.
very large, enormous	11.
an African mammal with a very long neck	12.
the way something is used	13.
very attractive, dazzling	14.
to claim as a fact but without proof	15.
learning, understanding	16.
a book used for keeping records of money transactions	17.
the amount of miles a vehicle has traveled	18.
transferring one's rights to a house as a guarantee that a debt will be paid	19.
a lower officer in the armed forces	20.
a special freedom to do a certain thing	21.

NAME ________________________________

C SENTENCES

In each sentence below, there is a blank corresponding to one of the words found in the word list. Write the missing word in the space next to the sentence.

Dad told us to keep our bicycles in the ___ while it was raining.	1.
When I ___ my sister's doll, Mamma made me fix it.	2.
Dr. O'Reilly, a famous ___, will perform the operation.	3.
The Indians thought the Sign of the Cross was a strange ___.	4.
Study hard so that you can win a ___ scholarship when you finish high school.	5.
We saw a very tall ___ when we went to the zoo with our cousins.	6.
"God made man in His own ___ and likeness."	7.
Grandma gave Stephen a ___ leather belt for his birthday.	8.
Uncle Donald is a ___ in the army overseas.	9.
Adam had the gift of ___ about all the animals in the Garden of Paradise.	10.
Our Lady was dressed in ___ clothes of gold, silver, and blue.	11.
Uncle Ambrose's car gets excellent gas ___.	12.
Saint Paul told the Christians to have ___ as they faced death.	13.
Mount Everest is the most ___ mountain God made.	14.
We had the great ___ of attending the pope's Mass in Rome.	15.

D STORY TIME

Read the following story, paying attention to the underlined words. Notice how they use the spelling rule to the right.

/**j**/ in **j**ump, a**g**ent, knowle**dge**

The Catholic Reform

Although the Protestants in Europe were wrong to revolt against the Catholic Church—the true Church of <u>Jesus</u> Christ—they did make some <u>just</u> criticisms of Church practices. The Catholic Church needed to reform itself and return to its founding principles. For that purpose, Pope Paul III called the Council of Trent in 1562. This Council decided to write down the dogmas of the Catholic Faith so that the differences between Catholic and Protestant beliefs could be easily known.

The Council also made <u>adjustments</u> to many practices within the Church. For example, the Council decreed that in order to <u>join</u> the priesthood, a man was required to spend several years studying in a seminary. If he went through the required training, the Church could believe that he had a sincere vocation.

Several faithful members of the Church were <u>overjoyed</u> to hear of these reforms. Many saints helped to bring about this reformation. One of these saints was Francis de Sales, who was the Bishop of <u>Geneva</u>. <u>Geneva</u> was a stronghold of the Calvinists. With great <u>courage</u> and determination, Francis de Sales did all he could to convert people back to the true Church. He used the new invention of the printing press to print pamphlets explaining and <u>justifying</u> the Faith.

St. Francis de Sales was a popular confessor among the many who felt <u>privileged</u> to receive his counseling. He wrote down some of his spiritual thoughts in the book *Introduction to the Devout Life*. Today, his sermons and letters are read and <u>enjoyed</u> by those who want to come closer to God in daily behavior, thoughts, and prayers.

THE TOWN AND CHURCH OF ANNECY, FRANCE

CLOCKWISE FROM TOP LEFT: CATHEDRAL OF THE VISITATION, THE ANNECY CANAL, THE MAIN ALTAR OF NOTRE DAME CHURCH, AND THE MAIN ALTAR OF ST. FRANCIS DE SALES CHURCH

ALCAZAR FOUNTAIN OF CORDOBA, SPAIN

THIS CASTLE IS WHERE COLUMBUS AND ISABEL FIRST MET.

LESSON

22

/ehr/ as in air

airy
cared
barely
baron
barrel
barrier
beware
carefree
carried
carrying
despair
embarrass
error
guarantee
marital
marriage
parallel
prairie
scarcely
tariff

BONUS

varies

NAME ____________________

The sound /**ehr**/ may be spelled **ar**, **are**, **air**, or **err**, as in **ai**r, b**ar**on, c**are**, and **err**or.

A SORT BY SPELLING

Each syllable has its own sound/spelling. Sort the words by the spelling of the sound of /**ehr**/.

ar	
are	
air	
err	

B DEFINITIONS

Given below are definitions to the words found in the word list. Write the appropriate word in the space provided next to the definition.

relating to air; atmospheric	1.
a mistake or inaccuracy	2.
almost not; scarcely	3.
differs	4.
the state of being married; union between a man and a woman	5.
a type of large container that has bulging sides	6.
having to do with marriage	7.
be cautious; watch out	8.
lighthearted, happy-go-lucky	9.
a tax on imported products	10.
transported or hauled	11.
transporting, hauling	12.
barely, hardly	13.
a giving up or turning away from God's mercy; to give up hope	14.
regarded highly; cherished	15.
to cause to feel uncomfortable	16.
to promise or pledge something	17.
a type of nobleman	18.
alongside; moving in the same direction the same distance apart	19.
a very large open plain	20.
an obstacle or barricade	21.

NAME ____________________

C SENTENCES

In each sentence below, there is a blank corresponding to one of the words found in the word list. Write the missing word in the space next to the sentence.

Because Jesus ____ about the hungry crowd, He multiplied the bread and fish.	1.
The husband and wife are celebrating ten years of ____.	2.
Please do not try to ride over Niagara Falls in a ____!	3.
Dad said that working too quickly in math can lead to____ in our answer.	4.
The road repairmen placed a ____ in the road.	5.
Our classroom is bright and ____.	6.
Our math teacher said that ____ lines are always the same distance apart.	7.
Mom always warns us to ____ of strangers.	8.
Jesus spoke with a woman who ____ her water jar to the well every day.	9.
Uncle Paul said his store will ____ a top quality product at a fair price.	10.
Pharaoh's daughter found a basket ____ the baby Moses down the river.	11.
Our Church teaches that ____ is a sin against hope.	12.
You will ____ your parents if you are not polite!	13.
The color ____ for many varieties of flowers, such as roses and tulips.	14.
Charles was ____ able to get out the door before it slammed shut.	15.

D STORY TIME

Read the following story, paying attention to the underlined words. Notice how they use the spelling rule to the right.

/**ehr**/ in **ai**r, b**ar**on, c**are**, or **err**or

Columbus

Columbus wanted to find a new sailing route to the Far East. He was anxious to sail west around the world to do this. Columbus took his intention to the king of Portugal, but the king was busy with other cares and would not help him. So Columbus went to Queen Isabel of Spain and asked permission to sail as a Spanish subject. She consented and paid for his voyage.

Isabel's agreement was due, in part, to the advice of her confessor. Columbus had been visiting a monastery, almost in despair because he could not find a monarch who would guarantee financial support. When the queen's confessor met Columbus at the monastery, Columbus spoke to him about his dream of sailing west around the globe to reach India. The priest was impressed by Columbus' courage and by his desire to bring the Catholic Faith to the people of India.

Since ancient times, it had been known that the world was round, but Columbus believed the estimation of the size of the planet to be in error. It had always been thought that a voyage around the world would take too long, and anyone who tried it would run out of food and water, unless they were fortunate enough to find some land between Europe and India.

Columbus set sail in 1492. The trip was difficult. Though they carried a great number of barrels of food and water, there was a shortage. Some of the men began to suffer from malnutrition and could barely work. His sailors grew discouraged and pressured him to turn back because of the scarcity of supplies, but he refused. As a result, instead of reaching the East, he discovered two new continents. More importantly, because of his discovery, many missionaries were able to carry the Catholic Faith to millions in the New World.

LESSON

23

/**eer**/ as in ear

appearance
career
cashier
irrelevant
irresistible
irrevocable
hemisphere
mysterious
perseverance
serial
serious
sincerely
smear
souvenir
spear
spiritual
fiercely
pierced
steer
superior

BONUS

weird

NAME ______________________________

The sound /**eer**/ may be spelled **ear**, **er**, **eer**, **ere**, **ier**, **ir**, or **eir**, as in **ear**, s**er**ious, car**eer**, sinc**ere**ly, cash**ier**, souven**ir**, and w**eir**d.

A SORT BY SPELLING

Each syllable has its own sound/spelling. Sort the words by the spelling of the /**eer**/ sound.

ear	
er	
eer	
ere	
ier	
ir	
eir	

B DEFINITIONS

Given below are definitions to the words found in the word list. Write the appropriate word in the space provided next to the definition.

a small trinket or article kept as a memento	1.
a person who runs a cash register at a store	2.
of high quality or importance	3.
not relevant; does not apply; unrelated	4.
having to do with the soul or spirit; not physical	5.
to spread over a surface	6.
the way something looks; its outward surface	7.
unable to be resisted; overwhelming	8.
punctured	9.
unable to be reversed; final	10.
one of the halves of the earth divided by the equator	11.
not easily understood	12.
a profession or occupation to earn a living	13.
in a violent or aggressive manner	14.
very strange	15.
keeping at a task in spite of difficulties or discouragement	16.
to maneuver or guide a vehicle	17.
in a series	18.
solemn; not to be taken lightly	19.
genuinely, honestly	20.
a long shaft with a blade or point on one end, used as a weapon	21.

NAME ______________________

C SENTENCES

In each sentence below, there is a blank corresponding to one of the words found in the word list. Write the missing word in the space next to the sentence.

The Church encourages us to pray for both physical and ___ help.	1.
My brother is studying medicine for his chosen ___ as a doctor.	2.
St. Theresa felt an ___ desire to visit Jesus in the convent chapel.	3.
My brother's pro-life essay was obviously ___ to the other essays.	4.
The United States is in the northern ___, while Brazil is in the southern.	5.
The ___ of her kitchen shows a great concern for cleanliness.	6.
We should pray for ___ in practicing our Catholic Faith.	7.
Father John told us that it is a ___ sin to disobey our parents.	8.
Saul ___ believed he was doing the right thing to persecute the Christians.	9.
Mom said it is ___ when I clean my room as long as I do it every day.	10.
Our baby sister will ___ the peanut butter on her face if Mamma does not watch her.	11.
I brought back a papal rosary as a ___ from Rome.	12.
The soldier at the bottom of the Cross thrust his___ into the dead body of Jesus.	13.
Deep sinkholes are just one of many ___ things we find on planet Earth.	14.
A driver must be alert if he is going to ___ his car safely.	15.

D STORY TIME

Read the following story, paying attention to the underlined words. Notice how they use the spelling rule to the right.

/**eer**/ in **ear**, s**er**ious, car**eer**, sinc**ere**ly, cash**ier**, souven**ir**, and w**eir**d

Exploration

When Columbus discovered the new land to the west, many people became interested in exploring farther. It appeared there was more land to discover. However, Spain and Portugal argued about who had the right to claim various areas. Therefore, Pope Alexander VI feared a war and agreed to settle their argument. While the king of Portugal continued to send sailors around Africa, Spain persevered and sent sailors directly west as Columbus had steered.

Columbus, when searching for a king willing to finance his trip, had approached the king of Portugal. However, the king was too busy to help him at the time.

One time, a Portuguese sailor was caught in a serious storm and was blown off course. The captain of the ship spotted nearby land and immediately claimed it for the king of Portugal. Thus it was that Portugal claimed one country, now known as Brazil, in all of South America.

Sao Paulo Cathedral

Sao Paulo, Brazil

Carmel Mission, California

The final resting place of Fr. Serra

LESSON

24

Suffixes -ity, -ical, -ly

basically
consecutively
curiosity
desirability
encyclical
entirely
evidently
financially
gratuity
heavily
immediately
opportunity
political
physical
practical
quality
quantity
skeptical
specifically
symmetrical

BONUS

likely

NAME

Some words end in -**ity**, -**ical**, or -**ly**, as in quant**ity**, phys**ical**, and entire**ly**.

A SORT BY SUFFIX

Each syllable has its own sound/spelling. Sort the words by the suffixes listed below.

-ity	
-ical	
-ly	

B DEFINITIONS

Given below are definitions to the words found in the word list. Write the appropriate word in the space provided next to the definition.

in a row; one after the other	1.
having to do with specifics or particulars	2.
appeal; attractiveness	3.
having to do with the body; having material existence	4.
completely; totally	5.
a chance to do something	6.
forming the basis; fundamentally	7.
according to money; from a financial point of view	8.
probable; expected to happen	9.
not lightly; weightily	10.
right away; in a moment's notice	11.
disbelieving; doubting	12.
an eager desire to learn; inquisitiveness	13.
exactly the same on both sides	14.
a letter put out by the pope to instruct the faithful	15.
having to do with politics	16.
relating to action and practice	17.
grade of excellence, how good it is	18.
the amount of something	19.
apparently; according to the evidence	20.
a tip or extra money benefit	21.

NAME ____________________

C SENTENCES

In each sentence below, there is a blank corresponding to one of the words found in the word list. Write the missing word in the space next to the sentence.

Little Jacob's ___ caused him to shake every gift under the Christmas tree.	1.
Grandma says it is not ___ to go shopping without a shopping list.	2.
St. Joseph made tables and chairs of high ___.	3.
Which pope wrote the ___ about the meaning of Truth?	4.
Aunt Alice looked ___ when Johnny told her the unbelievable story.	5.
Because of interruptions, Mary never had an ___ to tell her story.	6.
I turned the bottle of holy water upside down, but it was ___ empty.	7.
When Dad lost his job, his wealthy aunt was able to help us ___.	8.
Jesus endured great ___ suffering on the Cross.	9.
Jesus said that anyone who is ___ burdened should go to Him to find rest.	10.
Obey ___ when your parents ask you to do something.	11.
It is ___ that Momma will have dinner ready when we get home.	12.
When Henry played tennis with my brother, he lost three games ___!	13.
Our pastor keeps a great ___ of holy cards to give to children.	14.
My uncle gave several ___ speeches when he ran for state senator.	15.

D STORY TIME

Read the following story, paying attention to the underlined words. Notice how they use the spelling rule to the right.

Some words end in -**ity**, -**ical**, or -**ly**, as in quant**ity**, phys**ical**, entire**ly**.

Missionary

A Spanish Franciscan priest in the 1700s, Father Junipero Serra, was given the opportunity to be a missionary in the New World.

When Father arrived, he immediately began to establish missions. Other priests joined him, and many native Indians converted to the Catholic Faith. Father was responsible for establishing missions along the coast from Mexico to San Francisco.

Father Serra crossed miles and miles of land on foot, though the physical difficulties were many. It took Father forty-six days to cross the deserts and mountains to arrive at San Diego.

Father erected a large cross in San Diego. He celebrated Mass there and, according to one report, many Indians attended and "stood around in wide-eyed wonder and curiosity at the scene." Hymns were sung loudly and joyously by the Spanish, while soldiers shot their muskets into the air in celebration.

Father Serra established nineteen missions for the Indians along the California coast. The mission answered the practical needs of the Indians by teaching them how to farm, how to build homes, and how to practice the Catholic Faith.

When Father Serra died in 1784 at the Carmel mission, Indians came by the hundreds from far and near to place flowers on his dead body as it lay in his little cell.

LESSON

25

Soft sound of a, as in approve

approve
absorption
appeal
carnival
colossal
cordial
constitutional
international
achievement
martial
naval
official
oral
principal
vegetable
workable
assume
attendance
attractive
assign

BONUS

crystal

NAME ____________________

Some words contain a soft, unaccented **a**, as in **a**pprove.

A SORT BY SYLLABLES

Each syllable has its own sound/spelling. Identify the syllables in each word. Sort the words by the number of syllables.

2	
3	
5	

B DEFINITIONS

Given below are definitions to the words found in the word list. Write the appropriate word in the space provided next to the definition.

the act of soaking up, of absorbing	1.
charm; attractiveness	2.
an edible plant, such as a potato, lettuce, or squash	3.
capable of being worked, of being successful	4.
the number of people who are present	5.
very large; enormous	6.
to support; to accept as satisfactory	7.
warm and friendly; pleasant	8.
related to a constitution	9.
involving different countries	10.
a program of entertainment; a traveling group that provides amusements	11.
spoken; having to do with the mouth	12.
most important; chief; head of a school	13.
something accomplished or achieved	14.
having to do with war	15.
good-looking; charming; pleasing	16.
having to do with ships	17.
a clear, colorless, very fine glass	18.
a person who holds an office; one who enforces the rules in a game	19.
to presume; to take something for granted	20.
to appoint someone to do a task	21.

NAME ____________________

C SENTENCES

In each sentence below, there is a blank corresponding to one of the words found in the word list. Write the missing word in the space next to the sentence.

We must find a ___ solution to the problem.	1.
Momma looked very ___ in her new blue dress.	2.
The Battle of Lepanto was a great ___ victory for the Christian fleet.	3.
It was a great ___ for the disabled man to play basketball.	4.
The ___ means of obtaining grace is by receiving the sacraments.	5.
The painting did not have much ___ because it was so dark.	6.
The statue of David and Goliath was so ___ that it dominated the area in front of the art museum.	7.
I like to ride the ferris wheel at the ___ .	8.
Will Mamma ___ of this topic for my research paper?	9.
Will Dad ___ us a new violin lesson when we finish this one?	10.
The government ___ was working on his re-election campaign.	11.
Mom saved paper by giving me an ___ quiz on my spelling words.	12.
My grandmother gave my mother all of her ___ glassware.	13.
The jury must ___ that the prisoner is innocent until he is proven guilty.	14.
There was a great ___ at the Ordination Mass.	15.

D STORY TIME

Read the following story, paying attention to the underlined words. Notice how they use the spelling rule to the right.

Soft sound of **a** in **a**pprove

The Conversion of the Slavs

In the 10th and 11th centuries, the Slavic peoples were united under the leadership of the Kyivan Grand Princes, who ruled the vast territory of what is now Ukraine, Russia, Poland, and other Slavic countries. This period of history was marked by a high degree of civilization and development and was known as the "Golden Age of Kyivan Rus'." The people were known as Rusyny (not Russians).

In A.D. 988, Prince Volodymyr the Great, ruler of all the Rus', sent emissaries to Byzantium to learn about Christianity. They returned with missionaries who taught the people to know, love, and serve God. Prince Volodymyr accepted Christianity on behalf of his country and baptized the Rusyn population in the River Dnipro in Kyiv, the capital of the principality. St. Volodymyr believed in education and built many schools and churches.

Because Kyiv was continually invaded by the Mongols from the East, and eventually sacked, some of the Kyivan princes moved far up north and established their own principalities. One of the principalities was Muscovy (Moscow), which led to the birth of Russia as a nation. Russia accepted Christianity about a century later.

Up until this time, the Eastern Byzantine Churches were all in union with the one universal Catholic Church. Then, the Eastern Orthodox Churches broke away from Rome and recognized their own Patriarchs as heads. Eventually, the Slavic Orthodox Christian clergy came under the domination of the Russian czars. The control of the Church was carried to extremes with the rise of the Russian Empire under Peter the Great and Catherine the Great, who extended their rule over Rus'.

After the Russian Revolution of 1917, all religion was banned, and the newly assembled atheistic Communist government began to persecute all religious clergy and faithful, not just in Russia but in every other country it took over, Catholic or Orthodox.

Today, we must pray for the conversion of Russia and other Slavic nations as Our Lady of Fatima has instructed us to do.

Church of the Spilt Blood

St. Petersburg, Russia

MILAN CATHEDRAL

MILAN, ITALY

LESSON

26

Soft sound of e, as in item

absence
beneficial
consequence
correspondent
excellency
miscellaneous
modeling
modernize
novel
quarrel
label
chapel
strategy
supported
channel
client
colonel
confident
refuel
item

BONUS

judgment

NAME ________________________________

Some words contain a soft, unaccented **e**, as in it**e**m.

A SORT BY SYLLABLES

Each syllable has its own sound/spelling. Identify the syllables in each word. Sort the words by the number of syllables.

2	
3	
4	
5	

B DEFINITIONS

Given below are definitions to the words found in the word list. Write the appropriate word in the space provided next to the definition.

the act of forming an opinion based on the facts	1. ______
self-assured; sure of one's own ability	2. ______
defended as right or true	3. ______
the result of an action	4. ______
a book-length fictional story	5. ______
one who communicates news to a newspaper	6. ______
to make more modern or current	7. ______
title of a high dignitary in state or church; archbishop	8. ______
someone who provides business for a company	9. ______
assorted or mixed	10. ______
very important to a larger plan; a plan toward a goal	11. ______
a thing; a separate part in a list	12. ______
the art of forming clay or other substances; sculpting	13. ______
the state of not being in a certain place	14. ______
a difference of opinion; disagreement	15. ______
a tag attached to something to identify it	16. ______
a place for prayer	17. ______
a higher officer in the armed forces	18. ______
helpful, useful	19. ______
a waterway naturally formed between to land masses	20. ______
to provide fuel again	21. ______

NAME ____________________

C SENTENCES

In each sentence below, there is a blank corresponding to one of the words found in the word list. Write the missing word in the space next to the sentence.

When you greet an archbishop, say "Your ___."	1.
Our family ___ the pro-life candidate in the recent election.	2.
The race car was forced to ___ three times.	3.
The ___ ordered his soldiers to be careful not to harm women and children in the conquered city.	4.
We have a shoebox where we put ___ odds and ends.	5.
The families meet in the ___ on Fridays to say the Rosary.	6.
I read the ___ on the package before I bought the soup.	7.
Aunt Jean had to move into a hotel as a ___ of the fire in her house.	8.
Jesus said that a bad judge would eventually give a just ___ if the woman persevered.	9.
St. Peter was ___ that he would never deny Our Lord, but he did before the cock crowed three times.	10.
Grandpa says it is ___ to your health to eat an apple every day.	11.
We cannot go in the express lane if we have an extra ___ in our grocery cart.	12.
Mark Twain wrote the ___ *The Adventures of Tom Sawyer*.	13.
When Dad went to Fatima, Mom led the Rosary in his ___.	14.
The large city constructed a new ___ to change the direction of some of the water from the nearby river.	15.

D STORY TIME

Read the following story, paying attention to the underlined words. Notice how they use the spelling rule to the right.

Soft sound of **e** in it**e**m

St. Charles Borromeo

St. Charles Borromeo was the bishop of Milan, Italy, during the Catholic Reformation. After the Council of Trent, he was very willing to aid the pope in his efforts to greatly increase the holiness of the Church. By his example, he showed that valuable things and expensive living habits are not necessary for salvation. However, this comfortable way of living was not easily given up by some bishops. Finally, though, they realized Charles' daily Catholic life was more pleasing to God and many followed his example. Thus, St. Charles' efforts were successful.

LESSON 27

Third Quarter Review

LESSON 19	LESSON 20	LESSON 21	LESSON 22
attraction	accede	agent	airy
brochure	accelerate	allege	cared
chef	anticipated	budget	barely
Confession	Celsius	college	baron
construction	cemetery	courage	barrel
contribution	census	damaged	barrier
satisfaction	civilize	garage	beware
prescription	concede	genuine	carefree
efficient	conceit	gesture	carried
fascination	conceivable	gigantic	carrying
glacier	crevice	giraffe	despair
graduation	criticism	gorgeous	embarrass
impression	criticize	image	error
opposition	dominance	knowledge	guarantee
partial	fallacy	ledger	marital
pollution	masterpiece	mileage	marriage
possession	percentage	mortgage	parallel
potential	performance	privilege	prairie
precious	psychology	sergeant	scarcely
profession	replacement	surgeon	tariff
BONUS	BONUS	BONUS	BONUS
ratios	violence	usage	varies

- Pronounce each word for correct spelling.
- Say the word, spell it, and say it again.
- Divide each word into syllables.
- Take an oral pretest of all these words, then spell each misspelled word three times.

LESSON 23	LESSON 24	LESSON 25	LESSON 26
appearance	basically	approve	absence
career	consecutively	absorption	beneficial
cashier	curiosity	appeal	consequence
irrelevant	desirability	carnival	correspondent
irresistible	encyclical	colossal	excellency
irrevocable	entirely	cordial	miscellaneous
hemisphere	evidently	constitutional	modeling
mysterious	financially	international	modernize
perseverance	gratuity	achievement	novel
serial	heavily	martial	quarrel
serious	immediately	naval	label
sincerely	opportunity	official	chapel
smear	political	oral	strategy
souvenir	physical	principal	supported
spear	practical	vegetable	channel
spiritual	quality	workable	client
fiercely	quantity	assume	colonel
pierced	skeptical	attendance	confident
steer	specifically	attractive	refuel
superior	symmetrical	assign	item
BONUS	BONUS	BONUS	BONUS
weird	likely	crystal	judgment

LESSON

28

Soft sound of **i**, as in robin

accessible
affirm
eligible
evil
feasible
indelible
medication
permissible
positive
responsible
robin
sensible
susceptible
tangible
tennis
tepid
visible
worship
immigrant
immaturity

BONUS

ruin

NAME ____________________

Some words contain a soft, unaccented **i**, as in rob**i**n.

A SORT BY SYLLABLES

Each syllable has its own sound/spelling. Identify the syllables in each word. Sort the words by the number of syllables.

2	
3	
4	
5	

B DEFINITIONS

Given below are definitions to the words found in the word list. Write the appropriate word in the space provided next to the definition.

qualified or suitable	1.
a person who has moved permanently into another country	2.
to give the honor due to God	3.
unable to be erased	4.
to state positively or with confidence	5.
lukewarm; neither hot nor cold	6.
very certain; convinced	7.
easy to reach or access	8.
in charge; accountable for something	9.
not mature quality or state	10.
medicine	11.
very bad; wicked	12.
reasonable; showing good sense	13.
to wreck or spoil; destruction	14.
allowed; permitted	15.
at risk; having little resistance	16.
able to be done; possible	17.
physical; able to be touched	18.
a game played with a ball hit back and forth over a net	19.
able to be seen	20.
a small songbird	21.

NAME ____________________

C SENTENCES

In each sentence below, there is a blank corresponding to one of the words found in the word list. Write the missing word in the space next to the sentence.

Because of his education, John is ___to apply for the job.	1.
It is not ___ to jump into the pool if you can't swim!	2.
Momma washes my baby brother in ___ water so he is not too hot or too cold.	3.
Murder and other sins against the Fifth Commandment are very ___.	4.
We ___ God at Mass every Sunday at St. Matthew's.	5.
Is it ___ to travel in this snowy weather to visit the Shrine of Mother Seton?	6.
The Sacrament of Baptism puts a permanent, or ___ mark on the soul.	7.
Though angels have appeared to saints, angels are spirits and are not ___.	8.
The Moslems caused the ___ of many Catholic churches in Europe.	9.
He is prepared to ___ his beliefs before the crowd.	10.
My great-grandmother was a German ___ to America many years ago.	11.
Are you ___ you mailed the thank you note to Grandma?	12.
Every day, Brother John is ___ for ringing the Angelus bell for the monks.	13.
Tim's poor judgment is proof of his ___.	14.
My sister and I like to play ___ on the courts at the recreation center.	15.

D STORY TIME

Read the following story, paying attention to the underlined words. Notice how they use the spelling rule to the right.

Soft sound of **i** in rob**i**n

War for Independence

The new colonists in North America disagreed with the English laws governing them. They thought it was unjust for England to tax them, because the colonists had no representation in Parliament. They thought they were being ruled unjustly. The colonists wanted to be responsible for their own government in America.

They tried to present their sensible objections to the English king, but he would not listen. So these new colonies took on the impossible task of fighting the great British Empire. Under the leadership of George Washington, the Americans won a seemingly miraculous victory. The defeated English left, and the colonies formed their own nation, called the United States of America. The colonies were finally independent of English rule.

BALTIMORE CATHEDRAL

BALTIMORE, MARYLAND

Saint-Remi in Reims, France

Although closed by the French revolutionaries in 1790, it is a thriving parish church today.

LESSON

29

Soft sound of **o**, as in ballot

arbor
ballot
champion
condemn
conditions
confusion
connect
connection
consumer
custom
million
pardoned
piloting
prison
razor
recognize
Reconciliation
salesperson
symbol
patriot

BONUS

wisdom

NAME ____________________

Some words contain a soft, unaccented **o**, as in ball**o**t.

A SORT BY SYLLABLES

Each syllable has its own sound/spelling. Identify the syllables in each word. Sort the words by the number of syllables.

2	
3	
6	

B DEFINITIONS

Given below are definitions to the words found in the word list. Write the appropriate word in the space provided next to the definition.

a superior athlete; a winner	1.
someone whose job it is to sell something	2.
to denounce or disapprove of; to pronounce as guilty	3.
a design meant to represent something else	4.
tool with a sharp blade for shaving	5.
knowledge of what is right; good judgment	6.
surrounding circumstances; environment	7.
a place where criminals are locked up	8.
to attach or join	9.
to know or distinguish something	10.
a person who loves and supports his country	11.
the place where two things are attached or joined together	12.
someone who buys products for his own use rather than for resale	13.
a piece of paper used for voting	14.
Sacrament of Penance	15.
shelter of climbing vines or branches	16.
the way something is done; a habit or tradition	17.
the number which is a thousand times a thousand	18.
a state of uncertainty or disorder	19.
forgave	20.
steering or guiding	21.

NAME ______________________________

C SENTENCES

In each sentence below, there is a blank corresponding to one of the words found in the word list. Write the missing word in the space next to the sentence.

According to the census, there are over fifty ___ Catholics in the United States.	1.
It was wrong of Nero to ___ the Christians to death.	2.
The American soldier who died in battle was publicly recognized as a hero and a ___.	3.
The barber shaved the man's face with a sharp ___.	4.
There was much ___ at the Tower of Babel because no one could understand anyone else!	5.
St. Nicholas started the ___ of giving gifts at Christmastime.	6.
Is there a pro-life candidate on the ___ for this election?	7.
Before Jesus died on the Cross, He ___ the good thief who was dying next to Him.	8.
An angel rescued St. Peter from ___ where he was chained.	9.
If you ___ the dots in the coloring book, you will see a picture of Jonah and the whale.	10.
The two disciples did not ___ Jesus on the road to Emmaus.	11.
The bad weather ___ will prevent us from traveling to visit Uncle Leo.	12.
King Solomon was well known for his ___ and wise decision-making.	13.
The captain prayed to St. Christopher for help in ___ the ship during the storm.	14.
The ___ of the National Spelling Bee was a homeschooled student from Alabama.	15.

D STORY TIME

Read the following story, paying attention to the underlined words. Notice how they use the spelling rule to the right.

Soft sound of **o** in ball**o**t

The Beginning of the French Revolution

Some of the French kings in the seventeenth and eighteenth centuries did not rule for the people, but only for their own pleasure. They surrounded themselves with luxury. This cost much money. They had to raise taxes from the citizens to pay their expenses.

When Louis XVI became king, he began reforming the French government. Though France was already poor, he gave money to help the Americans in their war for independence.

The noblemen in France were used to their rich lives and did not like what the king was doing. The nobles aroused the people against the king because he was rich and they were poor. The people thought that this would make their lives easier, but instead it was the beginning of the horrible French Revolution.

Though the poor conditions of the people were not justified, no one could approve the murder and execution of innocent people. Reasonable people were forced to condemn such actions. Wisdom did not prevail and innocent people were put in prison for many months. While the confusion and chaos reigned for a time, many people today recognize the importance of remaining calm, praying, and voting for a better government.

LESSON

30

Soft sound of **u**, us; **u** before **r**, departure

accumulate
ambulance
anxious
conscientious
conscious
conspicuous
continuous
curious
departure
difficult
fracture
furious
jealous
miniature
unmatched
nervous
procedure
previous
signature
simultaneous

BONUS

zealous

NAME

The soft, unaccented **u** may be spelled **u** or **ou**, as in **u**s and nerv**ou**s. The sound of **u** preceding the letter **r** has a slightly different sound, as in depart**ur**e.

A SORT BY VOWEL SOUND

Each syllable has its own sound/spelling. Sort the words by the spelling of the sounds of **u**.

ous	
ure	
u	

B DEFINITIONS

Given below are definitions to the words found in the word list. Write the appropriate word in the space provided next to the definition.

unhappy at another's good fortune; envious	1.
a person's signed name	2.
the breaking of a bone	3.
occurring at the same time	4.
careful; done with careful attention	5.
anxious or tense	6.
awake; alert	7.
nonstop	8.
eager to learn; questioning	9.
the one that occurred before the current one	10.
very enthusiastic; showing strong support	11.
the act of leaving or going away	12.
not easy; challenging	13.
very angry	14.
much smaller than the usual size	15.
not equal; not similar	16.
nervous or worried	17.
obvious; noticeable	18.
to build up or gradually acquire	19.
the process by which something is done	20.
an emergency vehicle designed to take injured or sick people to the hospital	21.

NAME ____________________

C SENTENCES

In each sentence below, there is a blank corresponding to one of the words found in the word list. Write the missing word in the space next to the sentence.

Please write your ___ clearly on the legal document.	1.
They took Aunt Rose to the hospital in an ___.	2.
The Pharisees were ___ with Jesus because He scolded them.	3.
The lightning and the thunder were almost ___ during the thunderstorm.	4.
St. Paul was a very ___ preacher, continually traveling around from place to place.	5.
It may be ___ to become a saint but we are all called to be holy.	6.
You can play basketball when the ___ of your wrist heals.	7.
Dad likes to play on the golf course, but he took us to a children's ___ golf course.	8.
God tells us not to be ___, but to trust that He will take care of us.	9.
Thinking about going to the dentist makes me ___.	10.
Father Collins said that we should always be ___ in doing our work and saying our prayers.	11.
Babies investigate everything around them because they are very ___.	12.
The hostess said the flight to Rome is ready for ___.	13.
It is better to store up graces than to ___ all sorts of worldly goods.	14.
Daniel was thrown to the lions because some in the king's court were ___ of him.	15.

D STORY TIME

Read the following story, paying attention to the underlined words. Notice how they use the spelling rule to the right.

Soft sound of **u** in **u**s, nerv**ou**s;
u before **r**, depart**u**re

Napoleon Bonaparte

After the French Revolution subjected all of France to misery, Napoleon Bonaparte seized supreme power in 1795. He began the project of reorganizing the country. He first tried to mend the separation from the pope. However, his ideas were in conflict with the pope, so he had the pope imprisoned. This was his first show of power outside France.

Once Napoleon said he had a vision about his future. He said, "When I see an empty throne, I feel the urge to sit on it." Many of his friends, soldiers, and others distrusted Napoleon.

After Napoleon established peace in France, he did not confine his military campaigns to one country. He began to take over other countries as well. In 1798, Napoleon invaded Egypt, supposedly because he was insulted by the Egyptians. However, Lord Nelson's British fleet defeated the French fleet, and their blockade cut off Napoleon's supplies. He made much progress until the English defeated him in 1814.

L E S S O N

31

Words containing com

accommodate
accompanying
accomplish
combination
combine
comment
commitment
committee
commotion
community
companion
comparatively
compete
competitor
complement
complicate
compliment
computer
incomplete
recommend

BONUS

welcome

NAME

Many English words contain the syllable **com**, as in **com**bine.

A SORT BY SYLLABLES

Each syllable has its own sound/spelling. Identify the syllables in each word. Sort the words by the number of syllables.

2	
3	
4	
5	

B DEFINITIONS

Given below are definitions to the words found in the word list. Write the appropriate word in the space provided next to the definition.

unfinished; partial	1.
an electronic machine that stores data	2.
to suggest something favorably	3.
to make less simple; to cause difficulties	4.
to make up for something another lacks; something that completes	5.
going along or being together with	6.
measured by comparing	7.
friendly reception; to greet someone in a friendly manner	8.
a group of people living in the same locality	9.
to succeed or achieve a goal	10.
to make a comment that shows admiration	11.
a mixture or collection	12.
to mix or put together	13.
a friend; one that accompanies another	14.
to remark on something; to give an opinion	15.
a promise or agreement to do something in the future	16.
to adapt; to provide for something desired	17.
noisy excitement	18.
to strive for something, like a prize; to engage in a contest	19.
someone who is competing against someone else	20.
a group of people who decides something	21.

NAME ______________________

C SENTENCES

In each sentence below, there is a blank corresponding to one of the words found in the word list. Write the missing word in the space next to the sentence.

Mom won't allow us to leave our chores ____.	1.
St. Paul thanked Timothy for ____ him on his missionary trips.	2.
Did you help your sister ____ the ingredients to make a cake?	3.
The members of the parish gave the new priest a friendly ____ after his first Mass.	4.
We ____ for the spelling prize every year!	5.
If you make a ____, you must keep it even if it is difficult.	6.
There was a great ____ when the fox ran into the chicken coop.	7.
"I ____ that you read your Bible and say your Rosary every day."	8.
A ____ of nuns prays, works, and eats together.	9.
The Archangel Raphael was the ____ of Tobias on his journey.	10.
The innkeeper in Bethlehem had no room to ____ the Holy Family.	11.
Jimmy, please don't ____ matters by adding another project.	12.
The musical director gave us a ____ after he saw our Hungarian folk dance.	13.
It was not kind to ____ on your sister's mistake.	14.
I use the ____ to type my book reports.	15.

D STORY TIME

Read the following story, paying attention to the underlined words. Notice how they use the spelling rule to the right.

Many English words contain the syllable **com**, as in **com**bine.

St. Elizabeth Ann Seton

Elizabeth Ann Seton had a comfortable early life as the daughter of a Protestant doctor in the late eighteenth century in New York City. When her mother died, her father remarried. It was at this time that Elizabeth spent more time in spiritual reading and in prayer.

When Elizabeth was a young woman, she married William Seton who provided a comfortable living for her and the five children who were born in the first several years of their marriage. However, their fortune changed when William became very ill and died after a few short years.

Elizabeth was left with her five children. Due to problems with William's business, she was left with no money or financial support. In her distress, Elizabeth strengthened her spiritual life with more prayer. She had been interested in the Catholic Church before, and after she completed her studies, decided to enter the Catholic Church and to commit herself to living the Catholic life.

Elizabeth taught her children at home. She knew that her children were special gifts from God. Her mission was to keep guard over their spiritual lives. Even in her sorrow and poverty, she often played the piano while the children would sing. She was also a strict mother who insisted that the children obey her commands.

Finally, Elizabeth decided that she would like to teach other children along with her own. One morning at Mass after receiving Communion, Elizabeth said a special prayer, asking God to inspire someone to donate money to help her to establish a school to teach poor children.

Not long after, the bishop of Baltimore and a generous donor chose Elizabeth to establish a convent and a school in Emmitsburg, Maryland. Elizabeth immediately moved her children to Emmitsburg. Almost immediately, other women with a special vocation to teach children decided to accompany her. In 1809, Elizabeth Ann Seton founded the first American religious community.

NAME

LESSON 32

Words containing **ad**

- adapt
- adjourn
- adjective
- adjust
- admiration
- admire
- admissible
- admittance
- adorable
- advanced
- advancement
- advantage
- advantageous
- advertise
- admirable
- ambassador
- parade
- salad
- shadow
- stadium

BONUS

- tornado

Many English words contain the syllable **ad**, as in **ad**apt.

A SORT BY SYLLABLES

Each syllable has its own sound/spelling. Identify the syllables in each word. Sort the words by the number of syllables.

2	
3	
4	

B DEFINITIONS

Given below are definitions to the words found in the word list. Write the appropriate word in the space provided next to the definition.

to move parts so they match or fit	1.
to bring a meeting to a close	2.
a benefit; a trait that sets one ahead of the rest	3.
very cute or pretty	4.
a violent destructive whirling wind	5.
a large arena where sports games are conducted	6.
permission to enter	7.
beneficial; helpful	8.
respect and high regard for someone	9.
a dish made up mainly of lettuce and other uncooked vegetables	10.
to respect	11.
someone who represents a country; a diplomat	12.
the action of moving ahead	13.
to change to fit a new situation	14.
permitted or acceptable	15.
the darkness cast by an object that blocks the sunlight	16.
deserving to be admired	17.
moved forward	18.
a word that describes a noun	19.
a procession	20.
to promote or publicize	21.

NAME ______________________________

C SENTENCES

In each sentence below, there is a blank corresponding to one of the words found in the word list. Write the missing word in the space next to the sentence.

They dressed as angels when they rode on the float in the Christmas ____.	1.
We learned that in a diagram, an ____ goes on the slanted line under the noun it describes.	2.
Your little cousin is ____ in her white lace baptismal gown.	3.
Go to the storm cellar if you see a ____ coming!	4.
The Crusaders carried a banner of Our Lady as they ____ on the enemy.	5.
My brother is an ____ to any basketball team because he is so tall.	6.
It must have been difficult for Our Lady to ____ to a new life in Egypt.	7.
The pastor said it was ____ that the boys took food and clothes to the poor family.	8.
James wants to be the ____ to Spain when he grows up.	9.
Mom makes us eat lettuce and tomato ____ because it is good for us.	10.
Don't you ____ the mother for her sacrifice for her daughter?	11.
The sick in the streets were instantly cured when St. Peter's ____ touched them.	12.
Only the guests wearing wedding clothes gained ____ to the king's banquet.	13.
Please ____ the parts in the lawn mower so that it will work properly.	14.
Uncle Jerome took me to the ____ to see a baseball game.	15.

D STORY TIME

Read the following story, paying attention to the underlined words. Notice how they use the spelling rule to the right.

Many English words contain the syllable **ad**, as in **ad**apt.

Unions

After defeating Napoleon in 1815, England became more powerful. England became a great nation because of her victory. There were great advancements in factory production. England's factories, rather than farms, became the major source of employment. England was admired by other nations.

Millions of people began working in the factories as they believed the advantages were great. In some places, however, people were of the opinion that the workday was too long and the pay too little. This caused a division between the factory workers and the owners.

Then some of the workers decided to form a union, an organization to address the owners about their concerns. If everyone stood together to talk to the owner, he would be forced to honor their demands, or they could refuse to work. Thus, the owners were forced to treat the workers more fairly.

WESTMINSTER CATHOLIC CATHEDRAL

LONDON, ENGLAND

BROMPTON ORATORY MAIN ALTAR

LONDON, ENGLAND

LESSON

33

Words with the prefix **dis-**

discipline
disable
disagreement
disappointment
discourage
discovery
disaster
discuss
discussion
disease
disgraceful
disguise
dishonest
disinfectant
dissatisfied
distinct
distress
disturb
indispensable
disobey

BONUS

dismiss

NAME ______________________________

Many English words contain the prefix **dis**-, as in **dis**cuss.

A SORT BY SYLLABLES

Each syllable has its own sound/spelling. Identify the syllables in each word. Sort the words by the number of syllables.

Syllables	Words
2	
3	
4	
5	

B DEFINITIONS

Given below are definitions to the words found in the word list. Write the appropriate word in the space provided next to the definition.

Definition	
a difference of opinion	1.
not truthful; deceitful	2.
separate; different from others	3.
to lessen someone's courage or willingness	4.
failure to meet expectation	5.
the act of finding out	6.
a sudden great misfortune, such as a hurricane, flood, or tornado	7.
to make useless; to put out of action	8.
strict training that corrects behavior	9.
to talk about seriously	10.
trouble; misfortune	11.
to send away	12.
to upset; to interrupt	13.
completely necessary; essential	14.
discontented; not pleased with	15.
a substance that kills germs	16.
a serious talk or conversation	17.
a serious sickness	18.
shameful; dishonorable	19.
to refuse to obey	20.
something which hides a person's true identity; a costume	21.

NAME ____________________

C SENTENCES

In each sentence below, there is a blank corresponding to one of the words found in the word list. Write the missing word in the space next to the sentence.

St. Edmund Campion, being hunted as a criminal, was forced to hide his identity by wearing a ___.	1.
You must not ___ the ducks or they will fly away.	2.
In the hospital, they wash the floor with ___ to kill the germs.	3.
It was a ___ that Jane did not win the silver medal.	4.
It is ___ to pretend you agree with the personal attacks on others.	5.
Christopher Columbus made a wonderful ___ in 1492.	6.
The two candidates have a serious ___ about how to spend the money.	7.
St. Paul was willing to ___ with the pagans the fact that there is one true God.	8.
We had a long and difficult ___ about having a television in our house.	9.
Please ___ the smoke detector because Mom just burned the bacon!	10.
Jesus healed ten men from the terrible ___ of leprosy.	11.
Hurricane Katrina was a huge ___ for the city of New Orleans.	12.
Don't ___ your brother when he is learning to play the violin.	13.
It is ___ to throw a temper tantrum when you are ten years old!	14.
If they are disobedient, children cause ___ for their parents.	15.

D STORY TIME

Read the following story, paying attention to the underlined words. Notice how they use the spelling rule to the right.

Many English words contain the prefix **dis**-, as in **dis**cuss.

John Henry Cardinal Newman

Cardinal Newman lived in the nineteenth century. When he began to teach, he realized that his Protestant religion did not always seem logical. Many ideas had no good explanation. He had many discussions with other professors, but only the Catholic Church offered good answers. Though he was likely to be dismissed from his teaching job, he told the university that it was more important to receive Jesus in one Holy Communion than to keep his well-paid teaching position.

Cardinal Newman was a great leader of the Catholic revival in England. He was a capable scholar, teacher, administrator and religious leader. He used his writings to help the Catholic cause in England at that time. We can still appreciate what he wrote over one hundred years later.

NAME

LESSON

34

Words with the prefix ex-

exhausted
exaggerate
examination
examine
excavate
excavation
excellent
exception
excitement
exhibition
existence
exclude
expedition
expensive
exploration
explosion
extension
extra
extraordinary
extreme

BONUS

experience

Many English words contain the prefix **ex**-, as in **ex**amine.

A SORT BY SYLLABLES

Each syllable has its own sound/spelling. Identify the syllables in each word. Sort the words by the number of syllables.

2	
3	
4	
5	

B DEFINITIONS

Given below are definitions to the words found in the word list. Write the appropriate word in the space provided next to the definition.

to study closely or to inspect	1.
a journey or voyage	2.
something increased or extended	3.
a site which is being unearthed or dug up	4.
more; additional	5.
very good; outstanding	6.
a case that doesn't follow the usual rule	7.
completely worn out or used up	8.
a state of enthusiasm	9.
a display or demonstration	10.
out of the ordinary; unusual	11.
to overstate the facts	12.
costly; not cheap	13.
to personally observe an event	14.
to dig up or unearth	15.
a test to determine knowledge; a close study or inspection	16.
to shut out; to keep out	17.
the act of discovering new places and things	18.
the state of existing	19.
a sudden and loud bursting of chemical energy	20.
existing to a very great degree beyond the normal	21.

NAME ______________________

C SENTENCES

In each sentence below, there is a blank corresponding to one of the words found in the word list. Write the missing word in the space next to the sentence.

Jesus suffered ___ misery and pain on the Cross.	1.
Uncle Bill tells funny stories, but he has a tendency to ___.	2.
The temple Solomon built must have been very ___ because it was covered with gold.	3.
St. Francis Xavier went on a missionary ___ to Japan.	4.
We saw a beautiful ___ of religious art at the Vatican museum.	5.
You must study hard if you want to pass your ___.	6.
They began to ___ under the cathedral to find the bones of the saint.	7.
Grandma always prepares an ___ Thanksgiving dinner.	8.
Sometimes Dad makes an ___ and lets us stay up past our bedtime.	9.
I love to read stories about the ___ of the Spanish conquistadors and the priests who came with them.	10.
Please fix an ___ sandwich for your father because he is very hungry after work.	11.
Children are full of ___ around Christmastime.	12.
God keeps everything and everyone in ___ at every moment of time.	13.
After our long trip to Rome and the Vatican, we came home completely ___.	14.
Mom says we should not ___ the younger children from the party.	15.

D STORY TIME

Read the following story, paying attention to the underlined words. Notice how they use the spelling rule to the right.

Many English words contain the prefix **ex**-, as in **ex**amine.

God's Greatest Gift

At the Last Supper, Jesus instituted the Sacrament of the Holy Eucharist. It was during this Divine Banquet that the Apostles were ordained priests. They were carefully selected for the service of God and were given the power to change bread and wine into the Body and Blood of Christ.

On the following day, Good Friday, Christ died on the Cross between two thieves. On the Cross, Christ gave His life to save us. He rose from the dead in glory on Easter. Every day in the Mass, Christ re-presents His generous Sacrifice.

We offer the Mass with the priest as our supreme act of adoration. We ask for God's graces and thank Him for His blessings. He strengthens us in our trials and struggles, and He shares His love with all of us.

God expects us to love Him in return. We can express our love through prayer, through receiving the sacraments, and by helping others. Sometimes the poor and the sick are excluded from many social events because of their poor or sick condition. We can help the less fortunate experience God's love by spending time visiting and helping them.

The Tomb of Christ in the Church of the Holy Sepulchre

Jerusalem

Metropolitan Cathedral in Mexico City

It was the first cathedral in New Spain and the oldest one in the Americas. Hernan Cortes ordered a church built on the spot. The first church was demolished and this cathedral was started in 1567. The two towers were built with stones from Aztec temples.

LESSON

35

Words with the prefix in-

incidentally
inclined
instant
independence
indirect
individual
infection
inflammable
influence
informal
inoculate
inquire
installation
instruct
instruction
instrument
integrate
interdependent
interfered
interpretation

BONUS

invention

NAME

Many English words contain the prefix **in**-, as in **in**fluence.

A SORT BY SYLLABLES

Each syllable has its own sound/spelling. Identify the syllables in each word. Sort the words by the number of syllables.

2	
3	
4	
5	

B DEFINITIONS

Given below are definitions to the words found in the word list. Write the appropriate word in the space provided next to the definition.

right away; immediate	1.
to mix or blend together; to unify	2.
direction; schooling	3.
the state of being free from outside control	4.
an explanation or way of understanding something	5.
not direct; not straight ahead	6.
obstructed; to have taken part without invitation	7.
one person	8.
a disease or sore caused by a germ	9.
very easy to burn	10.
a new creation or device or machine	11.
a power of something or someone that affects another	12.
of minor importance	13.
to vaccinate or immunize	14.
the act of setting up or putting in place; something installed	15.
a device used to produce music; a tool or piece of equipment	16.
to ask or to question	17.
dependent upon one another	18.
having an inclination or tendency, willing	19.
to teach or educate	20.
relaxed or casual	21.

NAME ____________________

C SENTENCES

In each sentence below, there is a blank corresponding to one of the words found in the word list. Write the missing word in the space next to the sentence.

Children should be glad that they have parents to ___ them in virtue.	1.
I prayed for help with math, and that very ___, I suddenly understood the problem.	2.
Father Long gives ___ to the Confirmation class every Sunday afternoon.	3.
People everywhere want ___ from dictators.	4.
The doctor said that my cough was due to a respiratory ___.	5.
Our vacation consisted of a long and weaving ___ route to Washington.	6.
The harp is a beautiful ___.	7.
Mother Teresa of Calcutta was a good ___ on people throughout the world.	8.
We have an ___ dinner with our whole family every Sunday.	9.
The ___ of a peace force of soldiers on the border is aimed to stop the fighting.	10.
As a temporary visitor, I need to ___ about the Mass times on Sunday.	11.
Jesus did not seem ___ to turn water into wine until His mother asked Him.	12.
Each ___ was asked his opinion about the proposal.	13.
We should always try to ___ prayer in our daily routine.	14.
The wheel was a very important ___ over fifty-five hundred years ago.	15.

D STORY TIME

Read the following story, paying attention to the underlined words. Notice how they use the spelling rule to the right.

Many English words contain the prefix **in**-, as in **in**fluence.

From Spain to the New World

Spain's possessions in the New World covered a vast territory which included a notable portion of North America and, except for Brazil, all of South America. They also included the islands of the Caribbean Sea. Throughout this vast region, Spanish influence prevailed. The official language was Spanish, and it remains the language of the people today. Spanish laws, customs, and the Catholic religion were Spain's gifts to a great part of the New World.

The Spanish missionaries recognized that although the American Indians were superficially different from the Spanish immigrants, they were also children of God. The Spanish missionaries not only brought the American Indians the Catholic religion, but they gave them a sense of dignity as human beings and sons of God.

Although some abuses did occur, the Spanish did much good. When the Spanish conquered South America, they stopped many wars between the tribes, preventing many deaths among the American Indians. They improved the living conditions of the indigenous tribes by organizing communities, where they instructed the American Indians in new skills to make their lives easier. Eventually, the American Indians were able to be more independent, and were able to integrate into American society.

LESSON 36

Fourth Quarter Review

LESSON 28	LESSON 29	LESSON 30	LESSON 31
accessible	arbor	accumulate	accommodate
affirm	ballot	ambulance	accompanying
eligible	champion	anxious	accomplish
evil	condemn	conscientious	combination
feasible	conditions	conscious	combine
indelible	confusion	conspicuous	comment
medication	connect	continuous	commitment
permissible	connection	curious	committee
positive	consumer	departure	commotion
responsible	custom	difficult	community
robin	million	fracture	companion
sensible	pardoned	furious	comparatively
susceptible	piloting	jealous	compete
tangible	prison	miniature	competitor
tennis	razor	unmatched	complement
tepid	recognize	nervous	complicate
visible	Reconciliation	procedure	compliment
worship	salesperson	previous	computer
immigrant	symbol	signature	incomplete
immaturity	patriot	simultaneous	recommend
BONUS	BONUS	BONUS	BONUS
ruin	wisdom	zealous	welcome

- Pronounce each word for correct spelling.
- Say the word, spell it, and say it again.
- Divide each word into syllables.
- Take an oral pretest of all these words, then spell each misspelled word three times.

LESSON 32	LESSON 33	LESSON 34	LESSON 35
adapt	discipline	exhausted	incidentally
adjourn	disable	exaggerate	inclined
adjective	disagreement	examination	instant
adjust	disappointment	examine	independence
admiration	discourage	excavate	indirect
admire	discovery	excavation	individual
admissible	disaster	excellent	infection
admittance	discuss	exception	inflammable
adorable	discussion	excitement	influence
advanced	disease	exhibition	informal
advancement	disgraceful	existence	inoculate
advantage	disguise	exclude	inquire
advantageous	dishonest	expedition	installation
advertise	disinfectant	expensive	instruct
admirable	dissatisfied	exploration	instruction
ambassador	distinct	explosion	instrument
parade	distress	extension	integrate
salad	disturb	extra	interdependent
shadow	indispensable	extraordinary	interfered
stadium	disobey	extreme	interpretation
BONUS	BONUS	BONUS	BONUS
tornado	dismiss	experience	invention

Spelling Short Vowel Sounds

Vowel Sounds	Common Spelling Patterns	Sample Words	Some Other Spellings
/aa/ in **a**t	**a**	**a**t	**au** (l**au**gh)
/eh/ in **e**gg	**e, ea**	r**e**d, r**ea**d	**ai** (s**ai**d)
/ih/ in **i**t	**i, y, ui**	h**i**m, h**y**mn, b**ui**ld	**ee** (b**ee**n)
/ah/ in **o**x	**o, a**	**o**x, **A**men	**ho** (**ho**nor)
/uh/ in **u**s	**u, ou, o, oo**	**u**s, t**ou**ch, l**o**ve, fl**oo**d	**o** (s**o**n)

Spelling Long Vowel Sounds

Vowel Sounds	Common Spelling Patterns	Sample Words	Some Other Spellings
/ay/ in **a**te	**a, ay, ai, eigh, ey, ea, ei**	**a**te, h**ay**, r**ai**n, **eigh**t, h**ey**, br**ea**k, r**ei**n	**eig** (r**eig**n)
/ee/ in **e**ve	**e, ea, ee, ey, y, i, ie, ei**	**e**ve, s**ea**, s**ee**, k**ey**, hol**y**, p**i**ano, pr**ie**st, rec**ei**ve	**eo** (p**eo**ple)
/iy/ in **i**ce	**i, ie, igh, y, ui**	s**i**te, t**ie**, s**igh**t, b**y**, gu**i**de	**uy** (b**uy**)
/oh/ in **o**ak	**o, ow, ough, oa, oe, oo, ou**	s**o**, gr**ow**n, d**ough**, gr**oa**n, d**oe**, fl**oo**r, f**ou**r	**ew** (s**ew**)
/yoo/ in **u**se	**u, ew, eu**	**u**se, f**ew**, f**eu**d	**eau** (b**eau**ty)

Spelling Other Vowel Sounds

Vowel Sounds	Common Spelling Patterns	Sample Words	Some Other Spellings
/aw/ in **awe**	**a, o, aw, au, ough, oa**	c**a**ll, **o**ften, p**aw**, p**au**se, th**ough**t, br**oa**d	**augh** (t**augh**t)
/oo/ in **oo**ze	**oo, o, ew, ue, ui, ough, ou, eu**	t**oo**, t**o**, bl**ew**, bl**ue**, fr**ui**t, thr**ough**, gr**ou**p, n**eu**tral	**u** (tr**u**th)
/uu/ in b**oo**k	**oo, u**	w**oo**d, p**u**t	**ou** (w**ou**ld)
/ou/ in **ou**t	**ou, ow**	**ou**t, b**ow**	**ough** (b**ough**)
/oi/ in **oi**l	**oi, oy**	**oi**l, b**oy**	

SPELLING CONSONANT SOUNDS

Consonant Sounds	Common Spelling Patterns	Sample Words	Some Other Spellings
/b/ in **b**ell	**b**	**b**ell	**bb** (ra**bb**it)
/d/ in **d**a**d**	**d, ed**	**d**a**d**, lov**ed**	**dd** (su**dd**en)
/f/ in **f**an	**f, ph, gh**	**f**an, **ph**one, lau**gh**	**ff** (stu**ff**)
/g/ in **G**od	**g, gh**	**G**od, **gh**ost	**gu** (**gu**ard)
/h/ in **h**at	**h**	**h**ole	**wh** (**wh**ole)
/j/ in **j**am	**j, dge, g**	**j**am, fu**dge**, **g**em	**ge** (ca**ge**)
/k/ in **c**at	**c, ch, ck, k**	**c**at, s**ch**ool, du**ck**, **k**itten	**qu** (mos**qu**ito)
/l/ in **l**amb	**l**	**l**amb	**ll** (ma**ll)**
/m/ in **M**ass	**m**	**M**ass	**mb** (la**mb**)
/n/ in **n**u**n**	**n, kn, gn**	**n**o, **kn**ow, **gn**at	**pn** (**pn**eumonia)
/p/ in **p**et	**p**	**p**et	**pp** (ha**pp**en)
/kw/ in **qu**een	**qu**	**qu**een	
/r/ in **r**un	**r, wr**	**r**ight, **wr**ite	**rh** (**rh**yme)
/s/ in **s**at	**s, c, sc**	**s**ent, **c**ent, **sc**ent	**ss** (Ma**ss**) **ps** (**ps**ychology)
/t/ in **t**op	**t, ed**	**t**op, fix**ed**	**tt** (ki**tt**en)
/v/ in **v**an	**v**	**v**an	**f** (o**f**)
/w/ in **w**ise	**w, wh**	**w**on, **wh**ale	**o** (**o**ne)
/ks/ in bo**x**	**x**	bo**x**	
/y/ in **y**es	**y**	**y**es	**i** (on**i**on)
/z/ in **z**oo	**z, s**	**z**oo, i**s**	**x** (**x**ylophone)
/ch/ in **ch**ur**ch**	**ch, tch**	**ch**ur**ch**, wa**tch**	**ti** (ques**ti**on)
/ng/ in si**ng**	**ng**	si**ng**	**n** (si**n**k)
/sh/ in **sh**eep	**sh, ti, si, ci, ch**	**sh**eep, frac**ti**on, mis**si**on, spe**ci**al, ma**ch**ine	**ce** (o**ce**an)
/th/ in **th**is	**th**	**th**is	
/th/ in **th**in	**th**	**th**in	
/zh/ in vi**si**on	**si, ti**	vi**si**on, equa**ti**on	**s** (u**s**ual)

Spelling Rules for Consonants

The **/kw/** sound is spelled with the two letters **q** and **u**, as in **qu**iet. The letter **q** is always followed by the letter **u**.

The **/l/**, **/f/**, and **/s/** sounds after a single vowel in one-syllable words are often spelled **ll**, **ff**, and **ss**, as in be**ll**, stu**ff**, and Ma**ss**.

The **/k/** sound after a short vowel is spelled **ck**, as in qua**ck**, ne**ck**, qui**ck**, clo**ck**, and du**ck**.

The **/j/** sound after a short vowel is spelled **dge**, as in ba**dge**, ple**dge**, bri**dge**, do**dge**, and fu**dge**.

The **/z/** sound in **z**oo at the beginning of a root word is usually spelled **z** and never spelled **s**.

The **/sh/** sound at the beginning of a word or at the end of a syllable is usually spelled **sh**, as in **sh**eep and wi**sh**. At the beginning of any syllable after the first one, the **/sh/** sound is usually spelled **ti**, **si**, or **ci**, (except for the ending **-ship**, as in friend**ship**), as in frac**ti**on, man**si**on, and spe**ci**al. When the syllable before it ends in **s**, as in mis**si**on, it is spelled **si**.

All, **till**, and **full** are usually spelled with one **l** when they are added to another syllable, as in **al**most, un**til**, and care**ful**.

The **/v/** sound at the end of a word is never spelled **v**. It is usually spelled **ve**, as in ha**ve**.

Spelling Rules for Vowels

The **/iy/** sound is not spelled **i** at the end of most words.

The **/ay/** sound is not spelled **a** at the end of root words.

The **/ee/** sound after **c** is spelled **ei**, as in rec**ei**ve.

Phonics Rules for Consonants

The letter **c** before **e**, **i**, or **y** makes the **/s/** sound, as in **c**ent, **c**ity, and **c**ycle. It makes the **/k/** sound before **a**, **o**, and **u**, as in **c**at, **c**old, and **c**up.

The letter **g** before **e**, **i**, or **y** sometimes makes the **/j/** sound, as in **g**em, **g**iant, and **g**ym. It usually makes the **/g/** sound before **a**, **o**, and **u**, as in **g**ame, **G**od, and **g**um.

The letters **si** between two vowels can make the **/zh/** sound, as in vi**si**on.

Phonics Rules for Vowels

The vowels **a**, **e**, **o**, and **u** at the end of a syllable usually make the long vowel sounds **/ay/**, **/ee/**, **/oh/**, or **/yoo/**, as in p**a**per, b**e**gin, **o**pen, and **u**nit.

The vowels **i** and **o** often make the long vowel sounds **/iy/** and **/oh/** when followed by two consonants, as in k**i**nd and g**o**ld.

The vowels **i** and **y** at the end of a syllable sometimes make the short vowel sounds **/ih/**, as in rel**i**gion and bic**y**cle, but usually make the long vowel sounds **/ee/** or **/iy/**, as in rad**i**o, wind**y**, m**y**, and f**i**nal.

The letters **or** after **w** often make the **/uhr/** sound, as in w**or**d.

The **silent final e** causes the **preceding vowel** to make its **long sound**, as in m**a**de, **e**ve, d**i**me, h**o**pe, and **u**se.

The **silent final e** causes the **preceding c** to make the **/s/** sound, as in chan**c**e.

The **silent final e** causes the **preceding g** to make the **/j/** sound, as in chan**g**e.

Rules for Capital Letters

The first word in a sentence begins with a capital letter.

A proper noun begins with a capital letter.

The important words in titles of proper nouns begin with capital letters.

Interjections are usually capitalized.

All names referring to the true God and the Bible are capitalized.

The pronoun **I** is always written with a capital letter.

In the salutation of a letter, the first word and the name of the person begin with capital letters. In the complimentary close, the first word is capitalized.

Rules for Forming Plurals

Usually, plurals are formed by adding **s** or **es** to the singular noun.

Simply add **s** to most nouns.

Add **es** to nouns ending with **ss**, **x**, **z**, **ch**, or **sh**.

Change **y** to **i** before adding **es** when a noun ends with **y** preceded by a consonant. When a noun ends with **y** preceded by a vowel, simply add **s**.

Usually when a noun ends with **f** or **fe**, simply add **s**. Sometimes change **f** or **fe** to **v** before adding **es**.

Add **es** to a noun ending with **o** preceded by a consonant, except some words, such as piano**s**. When a noun ends with **o** preceded by a vowel, simply add **s**.

The same rules for plurals of nouns apply to verbs in the present tense, third person, singular.

Rules for Adding Prefixes and Suffixes

Past-tense words ending in **-ed** make the **/d/** sound or **/t/** sound when the root ends with a letter other than **d** or **t**; otherwise, the ending **-ed** makes the **/uhd/** sound.

Drop the **silent e** at the end of a word before adding a vowel suffix (prais**e**, prais**ing**).

Usually keep the **silent e** at the end of a word before adding a consonant suffix.

Change **y** to **i** before adding a suffix that does not begin with **i** (cr**y**, cr**i**ed).

Double the final consonant of a short-vowel one-syllable word before adding a vowel suffix (di**g**, di**gg**ing).

Double the final consonant of a two-syllable word ending with one consonant before adding a vowel suffix, except when the suffix changes the stress to the first syllable (refe**r**, refe**rr**ed, refe**r**ence).

When prefixes **dis**, **mis** and **un** are added to root words beginning with the same letter with which the prefix ends, this letter will be doubled (**unn**ecessary, **diss**olve, **miss**pell).

Rules for Identifying Types of Syllables

Closed Syllable (C)
ends with a consonant
vowel before the final consonant has a short vowel sound

Open Syllable (o)
ends with a vowel
vowel has a long vowel sound
can be just one letter if that letter is a vowel

Vowel-Consonant-e Syllable (vce)
final e is silent
vowel before **silent final e** has a long vowel sound

Diphthong Syllable (d)
diphthong (two vowels together) has one sound
diphthong syllable has one vowel sound

r-Combination Syllable (r-com)
at least one vowel followed by **r**
r gives the vowel a unique sound
r is after the vowel

Consonant-le Syllable (c-le)
syllable is at the end of a word
silent e is the only vowel in the syllable
syllable has no vowel sound
Only the consonant and the **l** are pronounced

Rules for Dividing Words into Syllables

A one-syllable word cannot be divided.

Each syllable has only one vowel sound/spelling.

Divide between the vowels when two vowels each make their own sound, as in qu**i**•**e**t.

Divide a compound word between the words.

Divide between the consonants when there are two or more consonants; however, do not divide two consonants that make one sound (a digraph) as in tel•e•**ph**one, or that blend together, as in sub•**tr**act

Divide before and after a vowel that makes its own sound, as in cav•**i**•ty.

Divide after the consonant when a short vowel sound is followed by a consonant and another vowel, as in H**eav**•**e**n.

Divide before the consonant when a long vowel sound is followed by a consonant and another vowel, as in p**a**•per.

When a word ends in **le** preceded by a consonant, divide the last syllable before the consonant, as in can•**dle** or fa•**ble**.

Divide between the base word and the prefix or suffix.

Rules for Accenting Syllables (for Parents)

Accent Mark
accent mark indicates the accented syllable

Accented Syllable
pronounced with a clear vowel sound

Unaccented Syllable
pronounced with a soft vowel sound

Primary Accent
strong stress on one of the syllables in a word

Secondary Accent
weaker stress on one of the syllables in a word

General Guideline
In two- and three-syllable words, accent the first syllable.
Then pronounce the first vowel as if it were a short, long, r-controlled, or double-vowel sound in a one-syllable word. If that doesn't make a recognizable word, accent the second syllable, and pronounce the second vowel according to its syllabic type.

ACCENT PATTERNS FOR TWO-SYLLABLE WORDS

Accent on the first syllable (' ___) The accent is usually on the first syllable in two-syllable words (**stan**'•dard, **sis**'•ter, **dol**'•lar).

Accent on the second syllable (___ ') Two-syllable words that have a prefix in the first syllable and a root in the second syllable are usually accented on the second syllable (ex•**tend**', con•**fuse**').

Accent on either the first or second syllable (' ___ or ___ ') If a word can function as both noun and verb, the noun is accented on the prefix (**con**' duct) and the verb is accented on the root (con•**duct**').

ACCENT PATTERNS FOR THREE-SYLLABLE WORDS

Accent on the first syllable (' ___ ___) The accent is usually on the first syllable in three-syllable words. The unaccented middle syllable has a soft sound (**vis**'•i•tor, **char**'•ac•ter).

Accent on the second syllable (___ ' ___) The accent is usually on the second syllable (the root) in words that contain a prefix, root, and suffix (de•**stroy**'•er; in•**ven**'•tor).

Rules for Accenting Syllables (for Parents)

ACCENT PATTERNS FOR FOUR-SYLLABLE WORDS (___ ___ '___ ___)

The accent is usually on the second syllable in four-syllable words (in tel' li gence).

ACCENT PATTERNS FOR SOME THREE OR MORE SYLLABLE WORDS

Accent patterns for words longer than two syllables are often governed by a specific ending pattern or an unaccented vowel.

Accent with the ending -**ic**

Accent the syllable just before the ending -**ic** (**fran**'•tic, e•**las**'•tic, en•er•**get**'•ic, char•ac•ter•**is**'•tic).

Accent with the ending -**ate**

In three-syllable words, the first syllable has a primary accent and -**ate** has a secondary (**in**'•di•cate)

In four-syllable words, the second syllable has a primary accent and -**ate** has a secondary (ac•**cen**'•tu•ate).

Accent with the endings -**tion**, -**sion**, -**cian**

Accent the syllable just before the endings -**tion**, -**sion**, and -**cian** (pol•**lu**'•tion, im•**pres**'•sion, ad•min•is•**tra**'•tion, e•lec•**tri**'•cian).

Accent with the ending -**ity**

Accent the syllable just before the ending -**ity** (**qual**'•i•ty, ac•**tiv**'•i•ty, per•son•**al**'•i•ty).

Accent in words with an unaccented middle **i** or **u** syllable

Accent the syllable just before an unaccented middle **i** or **u** syllable (**sim**'•i•lar, **aud**'•i•ence, par•**tic**'•u•lar).

Accent in words with an unaccented syllable containing **i**

Accent as /**y**/ the syllable just before an unaccented syllable containing **i** (com•**pan**'•ion, in•con•**ven**'•ient, mem•or•a•**bil**'•ia).

Accent in words with a final syllable containing **ti** or **ci**

Accent as /**sh**/ the syllable just before a final syllable containing **ti** or **ci** (fi•**nan**'•cial, pres•i•**den**'•tial).